# The Green Guide to Better Living

**Need2Know**

# The Green Guide to

## Ann & Terry Whitfield

First published in 2000 by **Need2Know**,
Remus House, Woodston, Peterborough PE2 9JX

Edited by Kerrie Pateman
Cover Design / Typesetting by Joanne Readshaw

# Contents

- Appliances
- Choosing your electricity supplier

# A Better Lifestyle

We have written this book in the belief that almost everyone can make some changes to enjoy a happier and healthier lifestyle, and at the same time help protect and improve the environment. If you have ever put down a newspaper or turned off the television news wondering if there is anything you *can* do without damaging something, then this book may be able to help.

As we write, arguments rage about genetically modified foods. Six months ago it was BSE. Every schoolchild knows that global warming, acid rain, the depletion of the rainforests and the erosion of the ozone layer are gradually destroying our planet. The sheer size and complexity of the problems makes most of us want to pretend they don't really exist or are someone else's business.

The good news is that taking positive action is something everyone can do and it does not have to hurt. Few of us want to go back to the days before cars, washing machines, televisions and health care. This book is not about denying the good things in life. In fact, living in a more sustainable way can make all our lives *more* enjoyable and fulfilling. It is certainly not necessary to eat muesli and wear sandals - and only one of us has a beard!

# Reasons for Change

There are many reasons why you might like to know more about green issues:

## Better health

You may have made the connection between how you live and personal health. If you are worried that pesticides in food could cause illness, you can avoid them. You may wish to know more about other food issues, including:

- genetically modified foods
- irradiation
- BSE
- antibiotics in animal feed

The green movement has much to say on all of these, but can also offer ideas about other health matters. These include how to avoid pollutants in the home, and avoiding stress thus promoting psychological as well as physical well-being.

## The health of the environment

These are usually issues which are not within a single individual's control, but you may well have recognised that they directly affect your personal health. You may also have made the link with concern for future generations. What kind of a planet will we pass on to our children and grandchildren? Some issues in this category are:

- habitat loss and species loss
- acid rain
- global warming
- deforestation
- depletion of natural resources
- waste
- nuclear waste

By informing yourself about these issues, you will be able to take action to ensure that you are not making things worse by your own behaviour.

## Ethics

Whether or not you are religious in the conventional sense, you may, like many people, be concerned that some things are unethical, and so want to avoid contributing to them. Such concerns are about:

- Animal welfare - including factory farming; animal testing
- Finance - ethical investments; third world poverty
- Peace - nuclear weapons; war; exploitation of third world countries.

# Developing Awareness

Going green is not something you can do overnight. It is about developing awareness and understanding of the issues, so that you can decide what is right for you. Many environmental issues are treated as one-off problems by the media. The truth is that they are inter-related, and largely caused by the way we live. You do not need a degree in ecology to make some simple changes which leave you healthier, happier and feeling less guilty!

# How to Use This Book

This book is designed to be used over a period of time, at whatever pace you feel comfortable with. The important thing is to make a start with what seems right for you and your family. You don't have to aim for perfection; there is nothing to be gained if you get disheartened because it all seems too difficult. The circumstances of your life are unique. Therefore, you are the only person who can decide what is appropriate for you. And your circumstances will change over time, so what suits you now may need to be changed in the future.

You will not find any pages specifically about global warming or the ozone layer. Instead, there are chapters about the essential activities of everyday life and how you can make changes to your lifestyle to benefit you, your family and the environment.

Each chapter contains a number of action points which will help you to put the chapter's ideas into practice. For those who want to go further, there is a list of organisations and recommended reading at the end of the book.

## Chapter 1

# Your Health and Well-Being

In this first chapter we make the connection between personal health, lifestyle and the environment. Often being kind to the environment is seen as an inconvenience or going without. But this is not really true. In fact, an environmentally friendly lifestyle is more likely to make you healthy and happy.

## Your Health and Well-being

Generally speaking, people in the Western world are living longer and healthier lives than ever before. Most people have enough food and live in decent houses. Much of the most arduous and soul de-stroying labour in factories and mines which killed our ancestors is no longer necessary. Women no longer toil long and hard to maintain a minimum standard of cleanliness in the home. Death in childhood is now a tragic exception rather than a common event.

Antibiotics and improvements in hygiene mean that for now at least, common infectious diseases are not the dreaded killers they once were. But the incidence of lifestyle related illness such as stress, anxiety and depression, heart disease and cancer is increasing.

### *Links between health and happiness*

There is a strong link between health and happiness and there is evidence that people are less contented now than they were fifty years ago. We believe that much of this discontent arises directly from the so-called 'consumer society'. None of us can completely escape from the effects of advertising and consumerism. But in this chapter we will give you some ideas about taking control of your life and assessing your needs rather than being manipulated by vested interests wanting to sell you a 'perfect lifestyle'.

## Six Steps to Health and Happiness

What really makes for happiness can also make for a sustainable lifestyle. There are certain key elements in achieving this. Below are our six steps to health and happiness, together with activities to help you think about how they can apply to your lifestyle.

For some activities you will need a notebook and pencil.

### *1. Take a long term view*

Modern life is complicated. There always seems to be too much to do and not enough time to do it. How often do you put off doing things which you would really like to do, because something else seems more pressing? We all seem to lead busy lives, and most of us feel pressured into rushing to fit as much as possible into an overpacked schedule. The result is that we rely more on the car, on ready-cooked, over packaged meals, and on machines and gadgets to speed things up. These make a huge impact on the environment, but rarely enable us to spend more time doing the things that matter.

**Activity – Personal Goals**

Think about your current worries and preoccupations. Write a list of your aims for the next week and the next month. Then ask yourself whether in five years time it will matter whether you achieved them or not. You will probably decide that some matter more than others.

For the important things, write down the reasons why they are important. These are things to which you should try to give priority, perhaps over things which seem more urgent at the moment.

## 2. Concentrate on activity instead of consumption

We are encouraged to spend most of our waking hours either earning money or planning how to spend it. We associate happy occasions with buying things. Christmas is the perfect example. But if you are not careful, every celebration will send you in a spin around the shops. There are decorations to buy, extra food and drink, expensive presents, new clothes... The list is endless. Try to live more simply, concentrating on 'doing' rather than 'getting'. The chances are you will be less stressed and have more fun as well as reducing your impact on the planet.

### Activity – Shopping hours

Over a month, keep a record of all the time you spend shopping. Remember to include browsing through mail order catalogues and the back pages of magazines, telephone and Internet shopping as well as walking round the shops and your weekly supermarket trip. Write down what you bought, and the time taken (including travel).

Next you need to assess whether your purchases were necessary or not. How much time did you spend shopping for things you did not really need? What else could you have done with that time?

Apply the five year test (see above) to your results. Shopping may be a pleasant diversion, but is it the way you want to spend your life?

## 3. Relationships matter more than things

It seems that modern life can satisfy all our material needs, but for many people does not lead to happiness and fulfilment. And it can never satisfy all our material desires! In this country we work the longest hours in Europe. Relationships suffer when we are so absorbed in the scramble for possessions that we don't have the time or the energy for the people we care about.

For example, parents are often under pressure to provide all the latest gear for their children. A recent radio item highlighted children who were ashamed of the family car being seen by their friends because it was not a desirable model. What kind of society have we created when children come home to empty houses because their parents are pressurised into working excessive hours to provide them with the latest type of trainers? Of course many parents on low incomes have no choice but to work long hours to provide a decent life for their families. However, many families do have a choice and in fact by consuming far more than they need make poorer families feel even more deprived.

### Activity – Treats!

Keep a list of treats for yourself and anyone else you may like to treat now and again. These can be anything at all – but must not involve long car journeys or retail therapy! They may be very simple, for example take a bath, go for a walk, visit a friend, pick some flowers from the garden... The important thing is to overcome the habit of associating pleasure with activities which involve consuming resources. Keep adding to the list as you think of new things. Eventually, you won't need the list any more, it will become second nature.

## 4. Get rid of clutter

Having decided not to clutter your life up any more with unnecessary purchases, have a look around your home with a new eye. As long ago as 1882, William Morris advised 'Have nothing in your houses that you do not know to be useful, or believe to be beautiful.' This advice is still good today. Most of us have a hoarding instinct, but having a house full of clutter means more work keeping it all in order. Having a good clear out from time to time seems to clear some space in the mind as well as physical surroundings. The things you no longer have a use for may be very useful to somebody else and may mean that they don't buy new. Recycling or re-using things is much greener.

### Activity – Throw out your junk

Go through each room thoroughly and pick out all the things that you have not used for a while and think you might not need any more. Pack them all away together in the loft or a cupboard and leave them there for six months. You should know after this time whether you want them or can get rid of them. Even with the best of intentions, you will probably need to repeat the exercise from time to time!

## 5. Get involved in your local community

When they talk about how life has changed, older people sometimes mention a lost sense of belonging. A generation ago, most people lived near their work, used the local shops and felt a part of the local community. Nowadays we live in a far more mobile society, mainly as a result of the motor car. In terms of increased opportunities for work and leisure this has been positive.

But we have paid a heavy price for this. People in towns, villages and neighbourhoods all over the country are fighting to retain a sense of community spirit. Sadly this often only comes to the fore when there are protests against new development or keeping open local schools. Whereas once upon a time it was taken for granted that neighbours would look out for one another, we now have to set up special neighbourhood watch schemes to combat crime.

Which of the following do you do? All are things that are likely to have a beneficial effect on your social life as well as benefiting the local area.

| | Never | Sometimes | Often |
|---|---|---|---|
| Support local shops | | | |
| Support local events eg arts events, fund-raising events etc | | | |
| Walk rather than take the car | | | |
| Car share with your neighbours | | | |
| Use local public transport | | | |
| Join local societies and/or attend their meetings | | | |
| Do voluntary work eg at your local school, hospital or charity shop | | | |
| Get to know your local park or nature reserve | | | |
| Take an interest in the activities of your local council | | | |
| Read the local paper | | | |
| Write letters to the local press | | | |
| Visit the library | | | |

Of the items in the never or sometimes columns, choose one or two to start with and begin to get involved.

## 6. Make connections

We have made the connections between health, happiness and the community, and know that the health of the environment can directly affect our health as individuals. But sometimes connections can be difficult to see. Modern life is so complex that cause and effect are not obvious. But every choice we make, whether it is about where we live, what we eat, what we wear, or where we go for our holidays, has a direct effect on the lives of others and on the environment.

These effects are rarely neutral. For example, buying products made from teak or mahogany from virgin tropical rainforests is clearly contributing to the destruction of those forests. However, many people don't make the connection, even if it is obvious, when they are buying their furniture. If they could see the devastation caused as a direct result of their action, they would be horrified.

Most decisions are much less clear cut. But, by educating ourselves about the important issues, we can start to make the world a better place rather than contribute to its destruction.

### Activity – Making links

The answers are given below, together with chapter references, where you will find more details.

Make the links between the following:

**1. Strawberries at Christmas and global warming**

   *a) the ozone layer*    *b) food miles*    *c) Santa Claus*

**2. Tumble dryers and acid rain**

   *a) power station*    *b) nylon shirts*    *c) deforestation*
     *emissions*

**3. Potato peelings and hotter summers**

   *a) methane gas*    *b) chip pans*    *c) soil erosion*
     *from landfill*

**4. The decline of the skylark and a cut price loaf**

   *a) plastic*    *b) intensive*    *c) decimalisation*
     *packaging*     *farming*

**5. Melting of the polar ice-caps and car exhaust emissions**

   *a) polar bears*    *b) toxic chemicals*  *c) global warming*

**6. New clothes and dead fish**

   *a) fabric dyes*    *b) globalisation*    *c) cod pieces*

The remaining chapters in this book set out the connections between our everyday actions and their effects on the environment. Although our individual behaviour may seem trivial at the time, when this is multiplied by whole societies, the effects are enormous. Our behaviour has implications for everybody, including people living in poverty in the developing world and all those who have not yet been born.

Links: 1. b) (Chapter 9)    2. a) (Chapter 8)    3. a) (Chapter 5)
       4. b) (Chapter 2)    5. c) (Chapter 9)    6. a) (Chapter 10)

## Action Points

✓ Make a list of 'green' activities you already do. This may include such things as using local shops, cycling or walking, using public transport or recycling newspapers. You may be surprised by how many things you are doing.

✓ Learn more about your local environment. You may live in a rural area or in the middle of a huge conurbation. Either way, it is a community – of people, plants and animals, with a history as well as a present. Consider which aspects you really value, learn more about them, and how to preserve and enhance them.

✓ Spend more time outdoors. You will be healthier, more active and will meet more people.

✓ Act locally. Take every opportunity you can to participate in your community, by supporting local arts events and activities rather than always travelling further afield for your entertainment and social life.

✓ Read the local paper. You will be able to keep an eye on planning applications and the activities of local businesses and councils. The sale of the school playing fields, the felling of local trees in the way of development or the building of new roads may seem to be purely local affairs with little importance for the bigger picture. But when this is happening on a national scale, as it is, then each small event takes on a new significance. Read Chapter 12 for more information.

✓ Take action! Letters to the press can influence a lot of people. Chapter 12 gives guidelines for writing letters.

✓ Be honest with yourself! Assess what you really can change and what you can't. It is all too easy to take the view that this is all very well, but I haven't the time, or I can't afford it.

✓ Apply the law of diminishing returns to your shopping habits. One new coat may be a necessity, two a luxury... but how much benefit do you really get from the next or the one after that?

✓ Remember that wealth is relative. Things that seem necessities today, were undreamed of luxuries only a few years ago. And by raising our own standards of living, we are contributing to that vicious and destructive cycle where greed becomes necessity and the poor are all the more aware of their disadvantages.

## Summing Up

In this chapter, we have suggested that happiness is a key component of good health. We have put forward five ways of improving your health and happiness. You have been asked to re-assess your lifestyle in relation to your goals, priorities and relationships. We suggested ways in which you can get involved in your local community. We have stressed the importance of making connections. Some of these connections are more obvious than others. As you go through the book, try to make connections for yourself. By raising your awareness, you will begin to feel more in control of your life.

**Chapter 2**

# Food and Health

This is the first of three chapters about food. In this chapter we explore the link between personal health, food and the environment. By adopting some of the ideas in this chapter you will be able to:

- improve your health
- reduce pollution caused by food transportation
- reduce pollution caused by manufacture of food, packaging and agricultural chemicals
- reduce packaging waste
- reduce animal suffering
- help our threatened wildlife

## You Are What You Eat

Food is plentiful and cheap, so why the constant reminders that food can be harmful? Although we live longer than previous generations, experts agree that it is largely because of better hygiene and antibiotics which destroy infections against which our grandparents had no defences. There is plenty of food in Western countries, but much of it is not healthy. Some serious illnesses such as cancer, heart disease and allergies are becoming more common, and many of these are linked to diet.

## *A good balanced diet*

It is often said that 'a good balanced diet' is all that is necessary for good health. But how many of us know whether we are eating a 'good balanced diet' anyway? The days when mother spent two hours toiling over the stove preparing the evening meal from fresh ingredients are long gone. 'Grazing' on snacks and relying on supermarket ready meals, many of us have no idea of what we are really eating.

**A balanced diet contains adequate amounts of**

- protein
- fats
- sugars and starch (carbohydrates)
- fibre
- vitamins and minerals

But it's easy to get the balance wrong, and eat too much sugar or fat, too much or too little protein, too little fibre or vitamins and minerals.

Manufacturing processes can make fat look like protein, remove all the fibre from carbohydrates and destroy vitamins and minerals (although some are put back later!)

If you eat a wide variety of fresh, rather than packaged, foods, with plenty of fruit and vegetables, along with wholemeal cereals, you will have a good balanced diet.

## Taking Responsibility

One of the great myths of the twentieth century is that our health is safe in the hands of science. We have been conditioned to believe that scientists know everything and, given enough time and money, can solve all our problems. One effect of recent food scares has been that people are finally questioning this and taking responsibility for their own health and well being. We can do this by becoming aware of what is in our food and improving our diet.

### Anna's story

When Anna's son Ben was 12 months old he developed severe eczema. Anna took him to see her GP who was regarded as something of an expert on skin complaints. She was given a tube of hydrocortisone cream and a large tub of emulsifying ointment. The doctor said that although it could be caused by something Ben was eating, 'food is so complicated nowadays' it was not worth investigating. Unhappy with this, Anna tried a simple process of elimination, which pinpointed eggs as the culprit. Ben's eczema cleared up, and the creams went in the bin. 'I couldn't believe the GP thought the diet of a year old baby would be so complicated that it wasn't worth sorting out at that stage. I hated the thought of him being covered in that awful rash and depending on steroid creams,' says Anna.

# The Fast Food Culture

Think of your perfect meal, and you will probably imagine a well-cooked meal of high quality ingredients. But shopping for and cooking fresh food takes time – a luxury many of us feel we cannot afford. Modern commercial interests are only too keen to encourage this view. Convenience food can be made to look just like the original, but anyone who reads the ingredients will find the resemblance stops there. Manufacturers rely on additives to make food palatable after they have done unspeakable things to it. Colours turn grey meat brown and brown peas green, emulsifiers make it smooth and create 'mouth feel', and preservatives ensure that it survives the long journey from factory to distribution centre to supermarket shelf.

### Salt and sugar

We are all victims of the insidious effects of the fast food culture. Salt and sugar are still the best friends of most food manufacturers, despite the bad press they get. Most salt and sugar we eat is in manufactured foods; banning salt cellars and sugar bowls would reduce overall salt and sugar consumption in the UK very little. Most of us are susceptible to salt and sugar from childhood. Once we become accustomed to highly salted or very sweet foods, it takes time to get used to eating food without – think of the difficulties dieters have giving up sugar in tea. So manufacturers pile in the salt and sugar to feed our cravings, and we keep buying their products. And when they take them away, they substitute chemicals which taste similar.

## Reading the Labels – is there such a thing as healthier convenience food?

Look out for misleading labels on pre-packaged foods:

- **Low sugar** foods usually contain artificial sweeteners. Of these, saccharin has been linked to bladder cancer and cyclamates have been shown to shrivel the testicles of laboratory animals. Other artificial sweeteners have also been linked to cancer in various studies.
- **Low fat** may mean lower in fat than a similar product, but still high in fat. For example low fat margarine may still contain 20-40% fat, along with other chemicals to make it resemble ordinary margarine. Low fat yoghurt may contain sugar, colour and thickener.
- **Low salt** food may contain chemical salt substitutes and may still contain a substantial amount of salt.
- **No artificial colours or flavours** almost certainly means it does contain artificial something else – check for sweeteners and preservatives.

## Why Dieting Doesn't Work

Being overweight is a major cause of health problems in the UK. And the diet industry is booming. But how many people do you know who have lost weight and managed to maintain their new weight over a long period? Unfortunately, so-called yo-yo dieting is worse for health than remaining a little overweight.

When most people go on a diet, they do nothing in the long term to actually change their eating habits. Fresh and whole foods contain more bulky fibre, which is good for health, and less fats and sugar. But dieters tend to remain dependent on manufactured foods, choosing brands with fewer calories, and trying to eat less. As they are not taking action to wean themselves off these foods, the weight soon creeps back on once they have finished starving themselves. The good news that it *is* possible to wean yourself off. It is very unusual for someone who has succeeded in giving up sugar in tea to want to go back on it again. But if they use saccharin tablets, they will never free themselves of the craving for sweetness.

## The Vexed Problem of Packaging and Waste

Packaging ensures that the food you buy arrives in good condition. It keeps food fresh and clean, even if it is transported half way across the world. It also gives the manufacturer the opportunity to provide you with information about its contents. Some packaging is obviously essential, although fresh, locally produced foods need very little packaging.

### Packaging Problems

- **Raw materials** – Many of the raw materials in packaging are not renewable. For instance plastics are made from oil; tin and aluminium cans are made from ore, all of which are finite resources.

- **Pollution** - All manufacturing processes cause some degree of pollution. Even paper and card manufacture can cause pollution to waterways. The smelting of aluminium and the production of plastic and polystyrene are all associated with environmental pollution

- **Tainting food** – There are concerns that some packaging can taint food. Some plastics, aluminium cans and lead seals in tins have all been suspect.

- **Transport** – Packaged foods are usually transported much further than fresh food, causing congestion and pollution.
- **Storage** – Refrigerated transport and storage uses even more energy and causes greater atmospheric pollution.
- **Disposal** – We produce mountains of rubbish, which is difficult to dispose of. Some packaging is re-used or recycled, but most of it we throw away.

---

# Is Eating Meat Healthy?

Meat, poultry and fish are all good sources of protein, vitamins and minerals. Red meat is an excellent source of iron, but also contains saturated fats known to be harmful in excessive amounts. Fish, on the other hand, is said to protect from certain cancers and other diseases.

Some studies have suggested that vegetarians are at less risk of developing heart disease, and some cancers. People become vegetarian for a number of reasons, and often because they are health conscious. They are therefore more likely to include a variety of fresh fruits and vegetables in their diets and take sufficient exercise. They are also less likely to smoke. So it may be for these reasons they are at less risk.

### So, what is the problem?

Well, the problem is probably not eating meat as such. There are healthy meat eaters, healthy vegetarians and healthy vegans (who not only avoid eating meat, poultry and fish, but also any animal products, including eggs, cheese, milk and even honey.) The problem is about *how much* meat people eat, and what happened to the meat when it was being produced. For example, intensively reared meat may contain chemical residues.

Plant foods contain fibre and vital vitamins (A, C and E) which are known to help protect against cancer. Whether you get your protein from meat and fish, or from beans and nuts, you will still have a healthy diet if you eat enough vegetables, fruit and fibre.

A person may become vegetarian or vegan because they believe it is ethically wrong to kill or abuse animals. They may be worried about the elimination of wild species such as fish by hunting. We became vegetarians many years ago, because we were concerned about animal rearing practices and the import of food from famine areas to feed British livestock. But from the point of view of health, it doesn't matter whether you eat meat or not. What does matter is the quality of the food you eat and the proportion of meat and dairy produce. Eat less red meat - and cheese and butter for that matter - to reduce your overall fat intake.

## What About the Environment?

From the ecological point of view, mixed systems of organic farming, rearing fewer animals but in an environmentally sensitive way, would best ensure the health of our countryside. Most British birds, animals and plants have evolved alongside traditional farming practices, and changes in farming methods have caused their catastrophic decline and in some cases extinction. A return to a less intensive, mixed system of producing animals, cereals, vegetables and fruit is the only hope for the skylarks, linnets, swallows and all the other birds and animals which grace our countryside.

Intensive farming is an ecological disaster as well as bad news for human health. In the next chapter we will look more at how improving your health can benefit the environment.

## Action Points

 Look at the contents of your weekly food shop. How much of it has been subject to processing? Can you reduce the amount of processed food you buy? Aim to eat a diet of simple, fresh food.

 Avoid packaging whenever you can. Packaging causes pollution. Simple, fresh food is likely to be less highly packaged.

 Try to reduce the amounts of fat, sugar and salt you eat. Allow your taste buds to recognise more subtle flavours.

✓ When you do buy tinned and packaged food, look for healthier versions. Organic baked beans are widely available!

✓ Rediscover the pleasures of cooking. There is plenty of help around - borrow a few cookery books from the local library and have fun experimenting.

✓ Set aside time to eat in a civilised way! Try to avoid grazing or eating in a hurry.

✓ Where possible buy locally produced food. This is better for the environment – think of the pollution caused by all those lorries and aeroplanes taking food around the globe. And better for you – the vitamin content even of unprocessed fruit and vegetables begins to fall as soon as they are picked. Check out your local markets and box schemes from organic farms. Do you still have a local shop where the shopkeeper knows where the food came from?

✓ Enjoy food in season, produced locally rather than shipped across the world.

✓ Investigate foods in your local health or wholefood store. Many of these will be less processed than supermarket foods.

✓ Buy organically produced food whenever you can afford it. And if your local shops don't stock it, ask why not. They soon will if there is enough consumer demand.

✓ Read the label. Generally speaking, the longer the list of ingredients, the more highly processed the food.

✓ Learn about additives in food.

✓ When choosing meat, fish, eggs and dairy produce go for quality (preferably free range and organically produced) rather than quantity. This will be better for your health, the animals and the environment.

✓ If you want to lose weight take a long-term view rather than starving yourself on crash diets and eating chemical substitutes for real food.

## Summing up

It really is true to say you are what you eat. But it is easy to feel that we are no longer in control of our food. We are too far removed from food production. We all know the stories about the children who are astonished to discover that milk comes from a cow.

By taking a few simple steps it is possible for all of us to improve our health and well being and in the process reduce the impact we have on the environment.

Changing diet is one of the first steps on the road to green living. By adopting some of the ideas in this chapter you can feel better, look better, and enjoy yourself more while creating less pollution. You will feel more in control of your life and well being and be on the way to being part of the solution rather than the problem.

## Chapter 3

# Food and Factory Farming

In this chapter we look at the links between farming practice, the environment and your health. We look at current controversies and what they mean for you. These include:

- Factory farming
- Irradiation
- BSE ('Mad cow disease')
- Genetically modified foods

## Food Scares

Most food scares follow the same pattern. A news story breaks, linking food with disease, raising the anxiety of consumers. Although reassurances are given, people remain suspicious and without accurate information, cannot take responsibility for their own food and health.

Whenever there is a controversy, the argument always goes: the product in question is safe to eat, until there is a proven link between it and some disastrous consequence. We've never felt that this level of assurance is good enough, and personally would avoid the product. In this chapter we give some very basic information about current food controversies, and point you in the right direction to find out more. You need to be well informed to reach your own conclusions.

# Factory Farming

The drive to increase food production during and after the Second World War still informs food policy today. This, together with an obsession with producing food as cheaply as possible, has led to industrial systems of agriculture. These farming practices destroy wildlife, degrade the environment and treat animals with appalling cruelty. Ironically, producing cheap food has generated unforeseen costs, picked up not at the supermarket till but by the taxpayer.

The production of maximum quantities of cheap food is achieved by:

- Large scale monoculture – Instead of mixed farming, huge areas of land are given over to the production of one crop. Tractors work efficiently and quickly over large fields without hedges and walls getting in the way.
- Using chemicals to control diseases and pest infestations.
- Bringing animals and poultry indoors to reduce labour costs and land use.
- Using land all the year round by over-wintering crops.
- Speeding up and increasing production using chemical fertilisers and growth promoters.

Food is certainly relatively cheap. The average household now spends less on food than on leisure. And in the EU we have more than enough food; to avoid food mountains, farmers are paid to 'set aside' land, keeping it out of production.

## *Arguments in favour of intensive farming*

- **Health** - We are now healthier than ever before. Surely this is something to do with the food we eat?
- **Safety** - Permitted pesticide residues on crops after harvesting,

washing and cooking are set by government at levels considered to be too small to cause harm.

- **Cost** - No-one need go hungry – intensive farming produces lots of cheap food, affordable by people on low incomes.
- **Hunger in the developing world** - Starvation is still a reality in other parts of the world. We need to develop systems to feed everyone. (Intensive farming shows no sign of achieving this in fact. The real reasons for starvation are political and economic.)

## The problems of intensive farming

- **Soil erosion** - Traditional farming replenishes the soil by adding organic matter. Chemical fertilisers do not do this. In addition, hedges are removed, which previously prevented the soil from blowing away and washing away when it rains.
- **Increased disease** - Diseases such as salmonella in poultry spread rapidly in intensive, overcrowded conditions. Arable crops, too, are more susceptible to disease when grown intensively.
- **Animal welfare problems** - Many people feel that keeping sentient creatures in battery cages and other cramped indoor units is disgustingly cruel. For example, battery chickens have to be 'de-beaked' to prevent them pecking each other.
- **Pesticide resistance** - Pests frequently adapt to the chemicals used to control them, necessitating the use of ever larger doses of stronger chemicals.
- **Antibiotic resistance** - Antibiotics are added routinely to animal feed. Unfortunately this excessive use has enabled bugs such as salmonella to develop resistance. When humans are affected by the resistant strain of a disease, antibiotics don't work.
- **Pesticide cocktails** - Although there are recommended limits on our intake of pesticides, no-one has researched the effects on human health of consuming different combinations of them.

- **Loss of wildlife** - Our wildlife has evolved alongside traditional mixed farming methods. Native animals, birds and plants are reliant on the hedges, ponds, small fields and woods which were a feature of the British countryside until a few decades ago. When these go, so does the wildlife.

# Food Irradiation

Irradiation is a technology which has been with us for some years, and uses ionizing radiation to prevent the deterioration of certain foods by delaying bacterial decay and killing insect pests. All irradiated foods are required to be labelled as such, but occasionally cases are reported when foods are found to have slipped through. There was an incident in 1999 when trading standards officers found that some shellfish had been irradiated and had not been labelled.

Irradiation can alter the texture and taste of food and destroy some nutrients. Some people fear it can cause cancer because of chemical changes to the food. It is clearly no substitute for good hygiene standards and eating fresh foods.

# BSE

### *The costs*

BSE – or 'mad cow disease' - hit the headlines in the 1980's, and has been a major news story ever since. There have been immense human and financial costs – 51 people are so far known to have died from the new type of CJD, (called vCJD) the human form of BSE. Billions of pounds of taxpayers' money have been spent on compensation for farmers, assistance to abattoirs, inspection and enforcement and research. Despite this, many farmers' livelihoods have been lost as a result of the disease.

### *The causes*

In order to increase milk yields and promote rapid growth, cattle are given protein-rich feed. When the Thatcher government abolished restrictions on the content of animal feed, animal offal was added as a cheap source of protein. It is thought that in this way scrapie, a brain disease affecting sheep, was transmitted to cattle, which then developed BSE.

Some experts believe that BSE was not introduced through scrapie, but was caused by organophosphate pesticides, used to control a serious parasite in cattle called warble fly. However, the continued use of animal proteins in cattle feed – including offal from infected cattle – caused more animals to be affected.

## Is beef safe to eat?

Massive, if belated, efforts were made to eradicate BSE. Feeding animal proteins to cattle was banned in 1988. All infected cattle and their offspring should be immediately destroyed, to prevent them entering the food chain. Suspect tissues from all cattle, such as the brain and spinal cord, are removed at the abattoir. Cattle are slaughtered before they are old enough for the disease to develop. The incidence of BSE is now decreasing. The Ministry of Agriculture assures us that British beef *is* safe to eat, although the link between BSE and vCJD is not generally disputed.

However, no-one can say that BSE has been totally eradicated, or that there is no chance of the infection appearing in the meat – or milk – of animals incubating the disease. Organophosphate pesticides are still used, and a new outbreak of warble fly could mean that they are once again used extensively. The link has not been proved or disproved. The fact is that scientists do not agree about these issues: some say beef is completely safe, others say they do not know for sure.

## Organic beef

The use of organophosphates on organic farms is banned. And organic farmers ceased feeding their animals with food containing animal proteins in 1983 - five years before conventional farmers. BSE *has* occurred on organic farms, but only where cattle from conventional farms have been introduced. These cattle could not in any case have been sold as organic meat (because they were not born and reared in the organic system).

## Genetically Modified Foods

Genetic modification allows scientists to take genes from one organism and place them in another. It differs from traditional crossbreeding because it makes it possible to transfer genetic material between species which are not related. This cannot be achieved through traditional breeding techniques. Genetic modification is much more precise than traditional crossbreeding.

This technique can be useful in medicine, (particularly the treatment or prevention of genetic diseases and growing organs for transplants) as well as in food production. Genetic modification can create crops which:

- last longer before they rot
- are resistant to herbicides
- contain built in pesticides
- are sterile (so that farmers cannot save seed from one year to the next)
- are drought, frost or salt resistant.

At the time of writing, no genetically modified crops are allowed to be grown in Britain for food use. But crops *are* grown for scientific purposes, to assess their impact on the environment. And most of us probably eat foods which have been genetically modified, because modified soya and maize are widely grown in the USA and in order to force people to accept them, the growers do not identify or separate them. These ingredients are in many basic foodstuffs, such as bread. They are also in animal feed – thus ending up in the food chain.

## The Objections to GMOs

### Health Issues

New foods which are considered to be 'substantially equivalent' (that is chemically the same as) traditional foods do not require any special safety checks – so GM foods do not have to be tested separately. However, some scientists are worried that genetically modified foods are not chemically identical, even though they have been supposed to be. For example, adding genes from nuts to other foods may cause potentially fatal results in someone who is allergic to nuts.

As far as health goes, the problem is that any new food can only be proved to be unsafe; it cannot be proved to be safe. And messing about with genes means that scientists can do just about *anything* to our food, and we will not know it unless they choose to tell us. For example, antibiotic-resistance genes have been used in GM tomatoes (for making purée) and GM maize. Some people not unreasonably fear that this may increase the problems of antibiotic resistance in medicine.

### Environmental Issues

There are serious concerns that have not been addressed concerning the effects of GMOs on the environment. Some of these involve the accidental release of modified genes into wild animals and plants; others involve the way in which they are used in farming.

Modified genes will almost certainly end up in the wild environment. Many wild plants are related to food plants and will crossbreed. No-one can possibly know what effect this will have, but it will certainly alter the ecosystem in some way.

Organic farmers are concerned that cross-pollination with their crops will mean the loss of their organic certification – no GMOs are permitted in organically grown food, even if they get there by accident.

Some genes give modified plants resistance to herbicides so that the whole crop can be sprayed. However, researchers are concerned that the weeds themselves may also become resistant (through cross-pollination with the resistant plants).

It was argued that herbicide resistant crops would reduce the number of applications of weedkiller necessary and therefore the overall amount of chemicals used. Of course, this has not happened. Farmers who know they can spray with impunity simply spray all the more!

Some crops have been modified to produce their own insecticide to kill devastating pests such as the Colorado beetle. This could mean a reduction in the chemical sprays used on food crops. But some scientists fear that target insects might develop resistance to the toxin, while beneficial insects such as lacewings and ladybirds – nature's own control system used to good effect by organic farmers – die.

It is impossible at this stage to say what the effects of genetic engineering will be on the environment. The danger is that we will end up with superweeds and superbugs and in the process lose the precious remains of our natural environment, already devastated by the changes in farming practice since the war.

### Animal welfare issues

Animals produced experimentally using genetic techniques have been prone to severe deformities and health problems. Dolly the sheep was one apparent success among many failures.

Genetic engineering has been used to produce a hormone called BST which can be given to cows to boost their milk yield. This is permitted in the USA but not (at present) in Europe. It is an example of how technology can achieve greater production at the expense of animal welfare. Cows produce up to twice as much milk, but as a result have enormously swollen udders and are more likely to suffer from lameness, mastitis and other infections.

### Issues in the developing world

It has been claimed that the problems of the developing world, where such devastation is caused by pests and drought, could be solved by GM crops. Maybe so, but the potential problems would be just as serious there. Investment in tools and irrigation, and changes to the economic system (which obliges developing countries to use their best land to grow cash crops to sell to the West) would achieve far more.

There remains the worry that the developing world could be further exploited by multinational companies seeking markets and resources without worrying about the potential for harm.

## Action Points

 Keep informed of developments in the food industry. You can do this by reading a good newspaper, and subscribing to one or more of the organisations listed at the back of the book, such as the Food Commission, the Soil Association and Friends of the Earth.

 Investigate for yourself the environmental and animal welfare effects of factory farming. Compassion in World Farming is an organisation which can tell you more.

 Read food labels and avoid ingredients which might be from genetically modified foods.

Only GM maize and GM soya *have* to be declared on the label as being from GM sources. Other foods from genetically modified sources (such as tomato paste and some food additives) don't have to be declared.

 Find out whether your local supermarket has joined the many to take steps to remove GM foods from their own brand foods. You will have to find out from them what their policy is. Do they label meat from animals fed on GM crops as being GM free?

 If you are concerned about any of the issues covered in this chapter, try to influence politicians and supermarkets (see Chapter 12). The labelling requirements (such as they are) for GMOs were only in response to public pressure, as was the action by supermarkets to remove them from own-brand products.

 Go organic as far as possible – read the next chapter for more information.

## Summing Up

The problems outlined in this chapter are technical and difficult. Many of them can be avoided by eating organic food – see next chapter.

A lot of people are angry about the way their food is being produced. They are fed up with health scares, the degradation of the environment, the unnatural manipulation of food by scientists and cruelty to animals on a massive scale.

We can't go back to the days before multinational companies dominated world food production, but we can do our best to keep abreast of current issues and influence political and economic decision makers. We can do this by the consumer choices we make, supporting campaigning organisations and writing to politicians and companies.

## Chapter 4

# The Organic Alternative

The Soil Association describes organic food as being 'produced from safe, sustainable farming systems, producing healthy crops and livestock without damage to the environment.

'It avoids the use of artificial chemical fertilisers and pesticides on the land, relying instead on developing a healthy, fertile soil and growing a mixture of crops. Animals are reared without the routine use of the array of drugs, antibiotics and wormers which form the foundation of most conventional livestock farming.'[1]

Because organic farmers do not rely on chemical solutions to combat disease and pests, they have to concentrate on promoting and nurturing positive health in their animals and crops.

## How Do You Know It's Organic?

'Organic food' has to meet legal standards. To sell food as organic, a grower must be certified by one of the agencies registered with the UK Register of Organic Food Standards (UKROFS). This is an inde-

1 Soil Association Website

pendent body mainly funded by the Ministry of Agriculture, Fisheries and Food (MAFF). The certifying bodies are:

- The Soil Association
- Demeter/Bio-Dynamic Agricultural Association (BDAA)
- Organic Farmers and Growers (OF&G)
- The Organic Food Federation
- The Irish Organic Farmers' and Growers' Association
- The Scottish Organic Producers' Association

Food certified by these organisations will either carry their own logo, or one of the following code numbers: UK1, UK2, UK3, UK4, UK5, UK6 or UK7.

There are stringent regulations and inspections at every step from grower to supermarket shelf. Organic farmers and growers must undertake a minimum two year conversion period before the food they produce can be labelled as organic. All imported organic food must conform to EU standards, and usually either the EU will have recognised the exporting country's organic standards or the exporter will have applied to one of the recognised certifying bodies above for certification.

## Confusing Labels

- **Free Range-** Free range is definitely not the same as organic! Free range means that the animals and birds are kept in slightly better conditions than battery livestock, including access to the outside during daylight. They may still be intensively reared, and treated with a similar range of chemicals.
- **Freedom Foods** - The RSPCA have introduced a labelling system known as 'Freedom Foods', which sets welfare standards for farm animals. Hens kept in battery cages and pigs in stall and tether systems are not allowed to carry the Freedom Food mark. This system gives some guarantees about the conditions in which animals are kept, but the standards are not as strict as organic standards.

- **Fairtrade** - The other label you might see on certain foods (particularly tea, coffee and chocolate) is the Fairtrade Label, awarded by the Fairtrade Foundation. This guarantees a better deal for small farmers in developing countries who produce these goods. Some Fairtrade goods are also organic, but others are not.

## Why Eat Organic?

Many people are eating organic food as the best means of protecting their health and the environment. There are a number of reasons for this:

- If you are concerned to avoid BSE and do not wish to cut out eating meat and dairy products altogether, the best way is to eat organic.
- If you do not wish to eat foods containing GMOs, the best means of guaranteeing this is to eat organic.
- If you wish to avoid chemical residues in foods it makes sense to eat organic.
- Organic foods are not allowed to be irradiated.
- Eating fresh, locally produced organic food is an excellent way of obtaining vital nutrients from your food.
- Organic food production protects the countryside and the environment. It works with nature rather than against it.
- Organic food production ensures the highest standards of animal welfare.

## 10 Reasons For Not Buying Organic Foods

Although organic food is becoming much more popular, there are still some reasons why people are reluctant to try it:

1 **It's expensive** – Sometimes true, but you are paying for high standards of animal welfare, and the certain guarantee the food you eat is not harming you or the environment. Sometimes it's

not true – local organic box schemes, for example, can represent excellent value.

2 **It can still contain chemical residues** – Yes, because of pollution in the air, water supply etc, but much, much less.

3 **Supply problems: you can never get what you want** – Well, yes. But the situation is improving, and many more farmers are applying to go organic in the wake of the BSE crisis. And there are many more manufactured organic foods available now too.

4 **Supply problems: you can't get food out of season** – True, we are so used to buying whatever we want whether it is in season or not. But this is improving, with more imports. The question is, do you want the food out of season? Food eaten in season is all the more enjoyable for not being available all the year round. And have you considered the pollution caused by transporting and storing all that imported food?

5 **Quite – what about food miles? 70% of organic food in this country is imported** – Yes, but again it's getting better. More government support is needed for farmers in this country wishing to convert – payments in the UK are one of the lowest in the EU. And there is no need to buy food which has been flown in just because it is organic.

6 **You can't taste any difference** – It depends. The sooner crops are eaten and the less distance they have travelled, the better they are likely to taste. Try eating freshly pulled organic carrots. It's a different experience!

7 **It is dirty, blemished and comes in odd shapes and sizes** - How important do you think this is? What is more important - blemishes you can see and can remove, or invisible chemical residues, many of which you cannot wash off?

8 **And full of insects!** – Where else can we veggies get our protein? Seriously, all that is needed is a little salty water to wash them in.

9 **There is no nutritional difference between organic and non-organic food** – This is difficult to establish, as there are so many variations in the soil. But over the years, an organic system puts back into the soil all the nutrients it removes, including trace elements such as manganese and zinc. This cannot be said for a conventional farming system, so logic suggests all things being equal, there will be more nutrients in organically produced food.

10 **It's just a middle class fad** – That's for you to judge. You've read the arguments, you make your choice.

## Our Top Ten Organic Foods

Start with our top ten organic foods! Even if you cannot afford to buy only organic food, these are good ones to begin with:

1 **Apples and pears** – Conventional crops are repeatedly sprayed with fungicides, insectides and a cocktail of other chemicals, and more fungicides are used to protect them during storage. Because of this, in 1995 the government recommended peeling non-organic fruit eaten by children.

2 **Carrots** – Again, carrots have been found containing very high levels of pesticide residues. And the organic ones taste so much better!

3 **Lettuce** – Non-organic lettuces are sprayed many times in their short growing season, to protect them from insects and disease. We find the presence of the odd slug very reassuring!

4 **Milk, cheese and other dairy products** - The pesticide lindane – known to be associated with breast cancer and banned in many countries but not in the UK – is often found in non-organic milk. Let's not talk about BSE again!

5 **Baby food** – Babies are more vulnerable to the effects of pesticides, as they are still growing. Their immature organs are less likely to be able to excrete harmful chemicals, and in proportion to their body weight, they eat much more than adults.

6 **Chocolate** – Once you have eaten organic chocolate the ordinary stuff will never taste the same again! Besides, conventional cocoa production involves very high levels of chemicals and pesticides (lindane was found in over three quarters of UK samples tested in 1995). Intensive cocoa production leads to deforestation, land erosion, and health problems among plantation workers.

7 **Manufactured foods containing soya, maize and tomatoes–** These are likely to contain genetically modified ingredients unless the manufacturer specifically guarantees otherwise. This includes most bread manufactured in this country.

8 **Wine** – Modern wine production is a far cry from the rural idyll of barefooted peasants treading grapes in the grounds of a Château. The vines are subjected to repeated applications of agrochemicals and the wine itself may contain various chemical additives, none of which are declared on the label. (Some traditional expensive wines are produced by more or less organic methods, but if you can afford them you can afford the organic stuff anyway.)

9 **Strawberries** – Before strawberries are even planted, the land is sprayed with an ozone-depleting chemical called methyl bromide. It is due to be phased out by 2010, but UK strawberry growers are lobbying to be allowed to keep it. (For more on the ozone layer, see Chapter 5).

10 **Bananas** – Most banana production uses massive amounts of agrochemicals causing enormous damage to the environment in Africa and South America. Organic bananas (mainly from the Caribbean) are becoming more widely available in some supermarkets.

### *Michael's Story*

Michael dreaded the winter. Every time a cold or flu virus was going round the office he caught it and would be ill for at least a week. He tried vitamin C tablets but they upset his stomach. His immune system was weak.

He knew his body needed some help to fight off infections and increased the amount of fruit and vegetables in his diet, even though he had never been very keen on them. More organic fruit and vegetables were appearing in the shops so he chose organic produce whenever he could and peeled the rest. He now eats mainly organic food.

Michael says 'I hardly ever catch a cold now and generally I feel much better and have more energy. I even find I enjoy eating fresh fruit and vegetables now – they taste much cleaner than the stodge I used to eat'.

## Where to Buy Organic Food

It is getting easier to buy organic food. Five years ago, you had to be fairly determined to track it down, but now it is widely available, although you still have to know where to look. You can buy guides which will give you specific information about where to look locally. The Soil Association also produces a national guide called *Where to Buy Organic Food*. In the meantime, here are some suggestions to put you on the right lines:

- **Vegetables** – Most supermarkets and some greengrocers sell at least a few organically produced vegetables. Other sources of organically produced vegetables (which incidentally are more likely to have been produced locally) are local markets, health food shops and farm shops. If you are lucky, you will be able to track down a box scheme from a local grower. For a set price each week, you will receive a selection of locally grown vegetables in season straight from the farm.

- **Fruit** – Unfortunately, there are very few organic fruit growers in Britain at present. Because of our climate, it is difficult to produce organically the unblemished, evenly sized fruit demanded by the supermarkets. However, as demand grows, more farmers are converting. Whenever you see any locally grown organic fruit, buy it! Imported organically grown fruit is easier to get hold of.

- **Dairy produce** – Most supermarkets now sell organically produced milk. If you have your milk delivered, it is worth asking your dairy whether they can provide organic milk – if they don't at present they might if enough people ask for it. Health food shops and many supermarkets stock organic cheese, butter, yoghurt and eggs.

- **Bread** – Many large bakeries now produce organic bread, and supermarkets' own brands often have at least one or two organic lines. There are also some producers of organic cakes and biscuits – ask in your supermarket or health food shop.

- **Groceries** - Frozen organic vegetables, ready meals, soups, tea, coffee, packaged foods, sauces, condiments and so on are now appearing in the supermarkets and health food shops. If you have a good nose around, you may be surprised at what you can find.

- **Meat and poultry** – If you don't live near enough to a specialist producer or a health food shop which can supply your meat fresh or frozen, you can buy organic meat and poultry by mail order. Some supermarkets are responding to demand and beginning to stock it.

*NB. Organic produce should be clearly labelled as such, and will have been certified by one of the organisations mentioned above.*

## Action Points

✓ Buy as much organic produce as you can.

✓ Buy locally produced food where possible.

✓ Learn to enjoy fresh food in season – strawberries and peaches are all the more delicious for not being available all the year round.

✓ Join an organic box scheme.

✓ If you can, try growing your own – organically of course!

✓ Put pressure on your local shops; keep asking them to stock more organic food.

✓ Make sure it is organic – ask questions and learn to recognise the organic labelling system.

## Summing up

People are no longer choosing food simply on the basis of price. They want genuine quality and real guarantees about how their food is produced. The best way to obtain these guarantees is to buy organic produce. You may feel it is not practicable for you to consume a wholly organic diet, but as you investigate the possibilities, you will realise the wide range of organic food available.

## Chapter 5

# Green Housekeeping

When we close the front door we like to think we are shutting out all the problems of the world beyond. Global warming, the ozone layer, acid rain and air pollution are all 'out there'. We can do what we like in our own home. It might be neat and tidy, or cluttered and cosy. But either way, we feel safe and in control.

Sadly, of course, this is not true. The individual choices we make in our own homes add up to create the global problems we are all aware of. And we cannot escape pollution by shutting the door. Our homes are full of industrial chemicals, and the long term effects of many of these are simply not known.

In this chapter we will be looking at:

- Reducing toxin levels in your house
- Reducing the amount of pollution you create
- Cutting down on unnecessary consumption.

## Reducing Toxin Levels - Is Clean Green?

Most houses are much cleaner nowadays compared to fifty years ago. We no longer rely on coal fires to keep us warm – central heating creates less dust and dirt as well as being easier and more convenient. Efficient vacuum cleaners and a host of cleaning products take the elbow grease out of housework. The result is a sparkling home that even the advert-land mother-in-law would approve of.

Kitchens have wipe-clean surfaces, fabrics and floorcoverings are treated with stain repellents and even furniture which looks like wood is actually easy-clean laminate. Every room has a range of special cleaning products designed to kill germs and remove every stain. And if any natural odours should survive this onslaught, there are air fresheners to disguise them.

Unfortunately, what we don't see is the chemical pollution caused by our obsession with cleanliness.

## Toxic chemicals in the home

The majority of cleaning products, air fresheners and paints release chemicals known as VOCs (see below) into the air. Furniture and kitchen units made from chipboard also give off a variety of VOCs. One of these is formaldehyde.

 **VOCs**

VOCs are volatile organic compounds. Hundreds of different chemical vapours are recognised by the US Environment Protection Agency as one of the greatest threats to public health.

Some health problems known to be on the increase are thought to be related to exposure to these chemicals, although it is difficult to establish causal links, as we are all exposed to different combinations of them. These diseases include breast and testicular cancer, childhood leukaemia, asthma, allergies and nervous system disorders.

The immediate effects of exposure to VOCs can include dizziness, headaches, nausea, respiratory problems and weakened immune systems. VOCs also contribute to atmospheric pollution – see global warming (chapter 8)

The good news is that it *is* possible to significantly reduce exposure to VOCs in the home, without going back to Victorian times when women spent all their time fighting a battle against dirt. Look in the Action Points below for some practical suggestions.

## Cigarettes
Cigarettes also produce poisonous gases – all smokers know the answer to this one!

## Children's toys
Even children's toys can contain hidden dangers. PVC (vinyl) contains chemicals called phthalates to make it soft. Some children's toys are made from PVC and the EC has warned that sucking and chewing toys such as PVC teething rings can be dangerous.

Phthalates can cause damage to the liver, kidneys and testicles.

# Reducing Pollution
We create pollution by our everyday activities. We discharge pollution into the atmosphere, the water supply, and polluting materials in the dustbin. To an extent this is unavoidable; we have to live, but there is a lot we could do to reduce the impact we have.

## *The atmosphere*
Everyone knows that Chlorofluorocarbons (CFCs) in aerosols and refrigerators damage the ozone layer. If your refrigerator contains CFCs (and most old ones do), this is not a problem until you come to dispose of it. When you do, you should contact your local authority for advice.

### The Ozone Layer
Ozone is harmful at ground level, but in the atmosphere it forms a protective layer which shields us from dangerous ultra violet rays from the sun. Ultra violet rays cause sunburn, can cause skin cancer

and cataracts and destroy plant life and plankton in the sea.

CFCs react chemically with ozone and break it down, and have created a hole in the atmosphere's ozone layer. This hole expands and contracts, but gets larger every year.

---

Although CFCs were phased out in Britain during the 1990's, some replacements such as the hydrofluorocarbons (HFCs) are important greenhouse gases, contributing to climate change. (See chapter 8) If you are buying a new refrigerator, ask what kind of refrigerants have been used. New ones safe for the ozone layer and the climate have been developed by Greenpeace. Aerosols are best avoided; there is usually an environmentally friendly alternative.

## The water supply

It is not only factories which discharge polluted water which ends up in the rivers and seas – so do we! The water that leaves your house through the drains goes to the sewage farm and after treatment into the river system.

### Buying detergents

In 1999 Ethical Consumer reported on washing detergents and pollution. They recommend that you look for soap-based detergents or ones with a high soap content. Read the labels carefully: use a product without phosphates, phosphonates or carboxylates as these pollute water and damage plants and animals. If you do buy mainstream brand laundry products, choose a powder rather than a liquid.

### Biodegradability

Most washing powders, washing up liquids and household cleaners make claims about biodegradability. But since it is a legal requirement that all such products are biodegradable, this is basically meaningless. It is important to look for products which are *rapidly* biodegradable. Usually these are plant-based, rather than made from petrochemicals. It is also important to use as little as possible.

## Surfactants

Surfactants reduce the surface tension of water. Although this is essential for the cleaning products to work effectively, they damage natural systems – plants and animals rely on the natural surface tension of water. Therefore it is important that the surfactants break down (biodegrade) safely and quickly before they reach the rivers and seas.

Most cleaning products nowadays have a panel giving details of the percentage of surfactants they contain. The lower the percentage of surfactants the less damaging the product. Try to use a product which uses plant-based surfactants only.

## Bleach

Bleach is a useful cleaning product. While it is effective in killing the bacteria in your toilet, it also kills the bacteria which digest sewage at the sewage plant. Avoid washing powders with added bleach; buy a detergent which does not contain bleach and add bleach separately if needed. Always use the minimum.

## *The dustbin*

Nearly everything you throw into your dustbin will end up buried in a hole in the ground (technically called a landfill site!)

All organic matter disposed of in this way rots down and produces methane gas. Methane contributes to global warming and is also dangerous to people who live nearby – it has been known to spontaneously explode.

The rest stays there indefinitely. This creates several problems. The first is that we are running out of places to bury the vast amounts of rubbish we create. The next is that all sorts of lethal and unpleasant chemicals are buried in there amongst the less harmful stuff. Discarded batteries for example, contain cocktails of damaging pollutants. Land so used remains polluted and unfit for use. Harmful liquids may leach into the water supply.

We are now running out of places to put the vast amounts of rubbish we produce, and the government is trying to find other ways of dealing with it. One proposal is to incinerate the rubbish. However, burning plastics and other pollutant materials can release dioxins and other very dangerous chemicals into the atmosphere. It also produces toxic ash which is a problem to dispose of – if buried it leaches chemicals into the water supply as well.

## So what can you do about it?

This depends on your circumstances. It may be possible for you to avoid putting organic matter into the bin by starting a compost heap – or donating your kitchen waste to someone who has one!

Always avoid putting hazardous items into the bin if you can. Your District Council should have a recycling officer who can advise you how to dispose of batteries. If possible, avoid using them in the first place. Use rechargeable batteries rather than disposable ones and use the mains if you can. Some batteries can be sent back to the manufacturer for disposal.

## Checklist – Reduce Refuse

How much do you recycle?

Give yourself a tick for each item you recycle. If you are unsure whether you can recycle it locally, contact your district council recycling officer.

| | |
|---|---|
| Glass | Aluminium cans |
| Steel cans | Paper |
| Plastic bottles | Carrier bags |
| Cardboard | Clothes |
| Shoes | Kitchen waste |
| Toner ink cartridges | Stamps |
| Furniture | Aluminium foil |
| Household appliances | |
| eg refrigerators, telephones | |

# Cutting Down on Consumption

With all this emphasis on recycling it is easy to lose sight of the fact that the best way of dealing with waste is not to produce it in the first place. By reducing clutter in your life, you can also save money, time and effort.

## The throwaway society

We live in an age of waste. In previous generations if something broke you would get it repaired. Nowadays, you are likely to have to replace it. If possible when buying new things, check whether they are repairable.

For our grandparents it would have been unthinkable to collect a new set of shopping bags every time they went for the groceries. If you invest in some proper bags, you will not have to worry about recycling carriers.

Think about how many things we regard as disposable which we would never have thought of in that way in the past. Why use tissue paper to wipe up spills, or paper hankies to blow your nose, when there are perfectly acceptable alternatives? A sandwich box with a lid is far better than aluminium foil or clingfilm for packed lunches. A re-usable bottle filled with fruit juice is cheaper and better for your health than a canned drink. There is no justification for our monumental waste of resources.

Disposable nappies liberated parents from the nappy bucket, but they create a huge amount of noxious rubbish. And they are much more expensive: using fabric nappies is estimated to cost £250 for one child, whereas disposables cost between £700 and £1,100. If cost isn't an issue, and you don't fancy dealing with them yourself, there are now nappy collection services in many areas, delivering freshly laundered fabric nappies.

## Packaging problems

Huge amounts of waste are created by unnecessary packaging. Items such as pens, toys, screws are all sold in superfluous bubble packs, which are difficult to recycle because they are made from a mixture of materials. If possible, find a shop where you can buy things loose. At our local DIY superstore, screws are packed in multiples of ten. At the small hardware shop in the high street, you can buy the exact number you want in a paper bag.

## *Junk mail*

Junk mail is another problem for green householders. It is far better to stop it in the first place rather than cart it all to the recycling centre. You can do this by contacting the Mailing Preference Service. If you send for postal offers, make sure you indicate that you do not want further information, unless you really do! You can stop free newspapers coming through your door by putting up a notice refusing them.

## *Conserving Water*

Droughts in recent years have brought home to people the importance of conserving water supplies. Your water company will be able to give you tips on saving water, but here are a few to be going on with:

- Use a bowl or put the plug in the sink when washing hands or dishes – don't leave the tap running
- Take a shower instead of a bath
- Put a water saving device in your cistern
- Don't leave the tap running while you are cleaning your teeth
- Make sure your dishwasher or washing machine is full before you use it
- Don't leave taps dripping – get them repaired promptly
- Use buckets rather than a hosepipe when washing your car
- If possible – avoid using waste disposal units; compost vegetable waste instead
- If you are buying a washing machine, dishwasher or shower, choose one which uses less water.

**Look for the Eco-label**

The Eco-label is awarded to products which have a lower impact on the environment. The environmental impact of the product from manufacture to disposal is assessed, and compared with similar products. At present the Eco-label can be awarded for:

- Textiles
- Light bulbs
- Washing machines
- Soil improvers
- Tissue products
- Laundry detergent
- Paints

## Action points

✓ Think carefully before you buy anything. Do you really need it? Will it improve your life or just add to the clutter?

✓ Choose natural materials where possible. These are less likely to contain unpleasant chemical compounds, are easier to recycle and will biodegrade at the end of their useful life.

✓ House plants help to reduce indoor pollution. NASA have done tests which show how plants can counteract pollutants in the atmosphere. Plants such as palms, pot chrysanthemums, rubber plants, ivy, fig, peace lily and spider plants all help to absorb VOCs. For more information, read Eco-Friendly House Plants.

✓ Try to avoid buying furniture and kitchen units made of chipboard. This may be easier said than done. One solution is to buy second hand furniture which is often much better quality than the modern stuff anyway.

✓ Aim to halve your weekly output of rubbish.

✓ Getting rid of furniture? The Furniture Recycling Network can advise you on furniture recycling projects locally.

✓ A number of organisations offer facilities for recycling empty toner ink cartridges from your computer. These include Action Aid, Tonertec (who give a donation for each cartridge recycled to Friends of the Earth) and Help the Aged.

✓ If you are upgrading your computer, consider donating your old one (if it's in working order) to Techknowledgy, who are working to enable people in the developing world to benefit from technology.

✓ Contact the recycling officer at your local district council to find out exactly what recycling facilities exist in your area. Agitate for better facilities!

✓ Find out whether your local WI can re-use jam jars.

✓ Use charity shops. Don't bin things they might be able to sell. Buy from charity shops too, rather than buying new.

✓ Check out the possibilities for refilling bottles and jars. Health food shops may sell loose honey, juices and oil. In many areas, the traditional milk delivery service still uses refillable bottles. You may be able to get laundry detergent and washing up liquid in refillable bottles. Failing this, buy it in big containers and refill your own smaller ones at home.

✓ Help to create a market for recycled goods. Buy recycled products whenever you can.

✓ Read the tips for conserving water and choose and act on at least two which you do not do at present.

✓ Contact Wastewatch, a free information service on all aspects of reducing, re-using and recycling waste, or look at their excellent website.

## Summing Up

There are many ways of improving your green housekeeping. Remember you don't have to do everything at once! Begin by doing whatever seems easiest. Every step you take can help to protect the environment.

Make your home a more natural place. While cleanliness and hygiene are important, try to keep a sense of proportion. You may do more to protect your health by avoiding chemicals than by obsessively trying to eliminate every last bacteria.

Keep in mind the ways to avoid waste:

- Reduce consumption
- Repair
- Re-use
- Recycle

And then dispose of the rest carefully.

## Chapter 6

# In the Garden

Imagine a nature reserve of a million hectares. This is the amount of land taken up by gardens in Britain. Gardens are becoming increasingly important both for us, and the wildlife we share them with.

However small, your garden is your own little bit of the planet, and how you treat it should reflect your care for the earth. You can choose either to poison it, or make it an ecologically friendly haven for wild animals and birds. This is one area where you can make a huge difference to your local ecosystem with a little thought and very little effort. You may find, in fact, that making your garden attractive to wildlife results in less work rather than more!

Even if your garden is tiny or you live in a flat, you can still grow plants and feed the birds. Your actions *do* make a difference. And the more you are surrounded by concrete, the more important it is to see something natural.

In this chapter we look at how you can create a *truly* green garden.

## A Tale of Two Gardens

The Brown family and the Green family live next door to each other. They both have medium sized suburban gardens but have very different approaches to gardening.

## The Browns' garden

The Browns are very enthusiastic and spend a lot of time working in their garden. Most of their garden is given over to lawn and flowerbeds. Every year they grow bedding plants from seed in peat compost and plant them out in the newly dug borders. They tend them carefully throughout the spring and summer, feeding with fertilisers and spraying regularly with insecticides. The tender plants are watered copiously and the Browns scatter slug pellets around the borders. There are a few permanent plants in the garden and these are mainly exotic species chosen for their striking flowers or foliage. These are also protected by spraying regularly against disease and insects.

The centrepiece of the front garden is a rockery made from Yorkshire Dales limestone. This was expensive but the Browns feel it was worth the price, particularly as it reminds them of a past holiday in the Dales.

The Browns are particularly keen on their lawn and take great care of it. Every year, to keep it looking perfect they apply special fertiliser, moss killer and selective weed killer. Persistent weeds are dealt·with by a spot weedkiller. To stop the lawn being spoilt by worm casts the Browns apply wormkiller. They mow it close twice a week and water it with a sprinkler after mowing.

The Browns' garden is surrounded by a privet hedge, clipped four times a year to keep it neat. However, they own an electric hedge trimmer so this is an easy task.

A couple of conifers provide height, but the Browns do not like deciduous trees because their leaves make a mess in autumn.

They used to have compost heap but they found it attracted flies and wasn't worth the effort since chemical fertilisers were so clean, cheap and convenient.

The Browns receive many compliments about their garden. People stop to admire the colourful summer displays and even in the winter when it is more or less empty it is always neat and tidy.

## The Greens' garden

The Greens also have lawns and borders at the front and rear of their house. Their borders are filled with bushes or perennial plants and the majority of these are species native to Britain. There are a number of small trees in the garden and a few annuals are sown directly on to the soil beneath them to add colour in the summer.

The boundary hedges are a mixture of hedging plants and again these are natives. They are given an annual trim but are generally allowed to grow bushy and flower. Campions, stitchworts and even dandelions are left to flower along the hedge bottom.

The lawns are cut regularly but the grass is not shaved close. There is moss on the shady parts of the lawn and it also contains a few weeds – the Greens actually like to see daisies in the lawn.

They have a large compost heap which takes all their vegetable peelings, lawn clippings and general refuse from the garden. They use the compost to grow new plants, and spread it around the bushes as a mulch. They also pile up their leaves in the autumn and allow them to rot down. In a quiet corner of the garden there is a pile of decaying logs.

There is a pond which teems with tadpoles every spring, but contains no fish. The Greens like to have birds in their garden, so they put food out daily and have nest boxes in their trees.

## Two approaches to gardening

The Browns read the gardening press. Gardening is their main hobby and having many popular gardening books on their shelves, they regard themselves as experts. However, their approach is complicated and involves lots of time and effort. Their garden uses up a large amount of resources but gives very little back in environmental terms.

The Greens favour a more relaxed approach. Their garden is largely self-sufficient. They feed their plants with compost made from waste products and do not need to buy chemicals to fertilise the soil or kill pests. The garden also contains trees which help to reduce global warming and provide a refuge for birds and insects. It is home to many native plants and animals, and although not a riot of colour every summer, is full of movement and life all the year round.

### Using Power Tools

Garden Centres are full of all sorts of machinery to make the job easier. Power tools, such as hedge trimmers and strimmers can be convenient, but try to use them only if you need them. They cause noise as well as pollution and use up resources. Petrol driven tools can be especially polluting. According to Ethical Consumer Magazine, using a petrol driven mower for one hour causes as much pollution as driving a large car for fifty miles. Electric mowers use only a quarter of the energy and do not generate emissions – but of course if you have the energy, a hand mower uses no power, gives off no emissions and provides free exercise!

## Creating an Attractive Garden

We enjoy our gardens more than ever these days. There are lots of books, magazines and television programmes telling us how to create a beautiful garden. However, a beautiful garden is not necessarily a healthy garden. Many garden 'experts' pay scant attention to environmental issues and the result is gardens which are attractive to look at but contribute little to a healthy environment.

For us, creating an attractive garden to enjoy and relax in goes hand in hand with encouraging birds and animals into it. We do not devote much time to our own garden and it is only an average sized suburban plot. Even so, we see birds all year round – feeding, fighting, displaying and nesting. In the summer we have several species of butterfly during the day and hedgehogs snuffling about on the lawn at night. Our tiny pond has a healthy population of frogs, tadpoles, snails, damselflies, backswimmers and all manner of unidentified creepy crawlies. A garden without movement would be a drab, lifeless place.

Once you have taken the decision to work with nature rather than against it everything becomes much easier. Rather than seeing a garden as a place where all sorts of harmful creatures and diseases attack your delicate plants you can relax and see it as an organic whole which, of course, is exactly what a well balanced garden is.

## A Mini Nature Reserve

Changed farming practices mean that wild birds and animals are increasingly dependent on our gardens in order to survive. Creating a wildlife garden is not complicated or difficult. Native species of plant, chosen to suit the conditions of your garden, will require a minimum of care and will attract a host of dependent wild species.

To attract wildlife, you need to provide food, water and homes:

- **Put out food and water for the birds** —You can do this all the year round, but remember that once you have started, you should continue as birds will come to rely on you. Water is just as important as food, especially during droughts or freezing weather. Buy peanuts from a reputable source, as mouldy nuts can contain toxins which kill birds. Some birds prefer food on a table, others on the ground. But make sure that you locate the food so that the birds have a good view all around, in case of cats. Move your bird table and hanging feeders from time to time to reduce the risk of infection, and put food out early in the day, so that it is all cleared away by evening to avoid attracting unwelcome visitors such as rats.

- **Create a garden pond** – No wildlife garden is complete without a pond. The bigger the better, but even a tiny pond will provide a drinking place for birds and attract frogs, dragonflies and all sorts of minibeasts. Make sure the pond slopes gently on one side, so that frogs and small mammals can easily get out. Any book about wildlife gardening will give further advice.

- **Grow plants to attract insects** – Butterflies and bees are suffering because of insecticides in the countryside. Plant native and traditional cottage garden flowers to attract them. For a wonderful show of late summer butterflies, plant buddleia and sedums.

- **Put up nesting boxes** – Nesting birds are a delight to have in your garden. Always put boxes well out of reach of cats, and out of direct sunlight. Detailed advice on this subject can be obtained from the RSPB.

- **Put up bat boxes** – Bats are no longer as common as they were. One reason is that they can no longer find suitable roosting places in old trees and draughty lofts. They will, however, readily use bat boxes. For more information, contact your local Wildlife Trust.

- **Make a log pile** – This is a place to put your larger tree prunings and provides a home for beetles, slow worms and hedgehogs.

## Growing Food

Even a small garden can produce a considerable amount of food if it is cultivated skilfully. Growing fruit and vegetables can be very satisfying and rewarding, but don't let anyone convince you that it doesn't require a considerable amount of work! The great advantage of growing your own, of course, is that you have complete control over how you grow it.

Naturally, we would recommend that you grow organic crops. Not only will this be better for you, it will not harm animals and birds. The Henry Doubleday Research Association (HDRA) can provide advice and information about growing vegetables organically, and produces a catalogue selling seeds and everything else you need to set up as an organic gardener. There are lots of books about organic gardening; a good selection can be obtained directly from HDRA. Our favourite is by Geoff Hamilton, and covers all aspects of organic gardening, not just growing food.

One of the delights of growing your own food is that you can cultivate varieties of fruit and vegetables no longer available in the shops. Many old varieties have superb flavour and have greater natural resistance to pests and diseases than modern hybrids. By growing these in your garden you can contribute to the preservation of traditional varieties which are in danger of becoming extinct. You can get more information from HDRA.

## Top tips for growing food

- Grow food which you cannot easily and cheaply obtain in the shops, such as organic strawberries and other fruits.
- Grow things which benefit from being picked and eaten straight from the plant, such as peas, beans and sweetcorn.
- Grow food and flowers together. It looks pretty and the insects attracted by the flowers will eat your caterpillars and pollinate your vegetables.
- If you are short of space, grow plants which you can pick over a period of time, such as courgettes and cut and come again lettuces.
- A nesting box for blue tits might encourage them to come and eat your caterpillars.
- Make a worm bin! The worms will turn all your kitchen waste into organic fertiliser. HDRA will tell you how.

# The Gardener's Seven Deadly Sins

**The following should be avoided at all costs:**

1 **Slug pellets** – These are an environmental disaster. Not only do they kill slugs and snails, they also poison thrushes and hedgehogs which prey on them. Incidentally, it is the small grey slugs that eat your lettuces; the large black and brown ones are harmless to growing plants.

2 **Peat** – Peat is taken from peat bogs which are an endangered natural habitat with unique flora and fauna. Don't buy it! *Gardening Which* tested peat-free composts and found some which were 'at least as good as the majority of peat based' products for growing new plants. Garden compost and leaf mould are far better as soil conditioners and cost nothing.

3 **Plants taken from the wild** – Always buy your native plants from a reputable company. Some plants, such as bluebells and cyclamens have been stolen from wild places in large numbers. Ask whether they are nursery grown.

4 **Plants which don't suit the growing conditions** – Choose plants which suit your soil and don't need excessive watering. Don't buy acid loving plants to grow in an alkaline soil.

5 **Gravel, limestone etc** – Quarrying destroys landscapes and habitats and uses a lot of resources in the process. Limestone pavements are an extremely rare habitat, home to some of our most beautiful wild flowers, and are destroyed just to put the stone into people's gardens.

6 **Chemicals** – These are damaging to your health and the environment. Learn to do without them! Healthy plants can often withstand a bit of damage from insects or disease. Don't worry about it - relax!

7 **Excessive tidiness** –Don't be in too much of a hurry to tidy up. Many creatures rely on decaying matter to live. Goldfinches will feed on your lavender seed heads throughout the winter.

## Action Points

 Make a compost heap – If you don't have one, you will have to put your garden and kitchen waste in the bin. It will probably end up in a landfill site where it will contribute to the production of methane gas. If properly composted, all this waste turns into a clean, sweet-smelling compost which can be used as an alternative to peat and chemical fertilisers. A good organic gardening book will tell you how to do this. Alternatively, contact the Henry Doubleday Research Association.

 Plant native shrubs and trees – These require less care and provide the essential conditions for native animals and birds to thrive. Choose appropriate species for the size of your garden.

You will probably have to buy these from a specialist nursery who will also be able to give you advice.

✓ Grow wild flowers – But don't collect plants or seed from the wild! Any specialist organic supplier or the HDRA will be able to help.

✓ If you own a cat, consider fixing a small bell to its collar to warn birds of its approach.

✓ Recycle things – Try not to let your garden be another reason for buying lots of things. Don't buy new if you can re-use something you already have. Plastic bottles cut in half make excellent cloches to protect tender young plants from hungry snails. You will no doubt think of other ideas.

✓ Car boot sales are a good source of plant pots, garden tools etc.

✓ Conserve water – Choosing the right plants will minimise the need for watering. Lawns don't need watering in the summer, they will soon green up when it rains. Hosepipes and sprinklers use over 500 litres in an hour. Use a watering can instead. And remember that water can be recycled –water from bathing and washing up is fine for plants. Or if you can collect it, rainwater is even better.

## Summing Up

Your garden is your own patch of the earth – make sure you make the most of it by creating a refuge for yourself and for nature.

By following the ideas in this chapter, you really can help to make the world a greener place. Your garden should not be just another way of using up resources.

It is not necessary to create yet another artificial environment in order to have a beautiful garden. Indeed the most beautiful and productive gardens are alive with natural movement and sound as well as colour.

## Chapter 7

# Doing it Yourself

As a green householder, you will be concerned to maintain your home to a good standard. A poorly maintained home is inefficient and deteriorates quickly, costing more resources, time and money in the long run.

The current fashion for home improvements can be an enjoyable way of improving our surroundings. However, unless we are careful, it is also another way of getting us to buy more – inevitably meaning that we consume more resources.

Modern DIY materials have been developed by the chemical industry for efficiency, ease of use and cheapness; but usually with scant regard for the environment at any stage of manufacture, use or disposal.

This chapter gives information about DIY materials to help you maintain and improve your home with the minimum impact on the environment and on your health.

## Health and Safety - Undoing the Past

Some materials which can still be found in older houses are extremely hazardous:

- Lead pipes are sometimes found in older plumbing systems and should be replaced as soon as possible.

- Lead is also found in old paint, and great care should be taken when rubbing down or stripping old painted surfaces not to inhale the dust or fumes. If you are worried about lead paint in your home, contact your environmental health department at your district council for advice.
- In the past, asbestos was used extensively in building materials. If you suspect that you have a problem with asbestos in your home, it must be dealt with by a professional. Contact environmental health.

# Choosing Paints

Have a look through the paint cans at your DIY shop. You will see a variety of safety, health and environmental information on the labels. These will tell you whether the paint is water, oil or solvent based.

On all paint you will read warnings about working only in well ventilated areas. You will be warned not to empty the paint into drains or watercourses. In the case of solvent based paints, you may see a logo indicating that the paint has a high VOC content (see Chapter 5). These are likely to be released into the atmosphere in your home at high levels during application and drying, and will continue to be present afterwards for weeks or months, in decreasing amounts.

### Water based paints

Although water based paints may be sold as containing minimal or low levels of VOCs, they can still cause indoor air pollution. Most modern water-based paints contain fungicides and bactericides causing toxic fumes to be released into the air.

### Oil based paints

These paints are likely to contain higher levels of VOCs than water based paints, but lower levels than solvent based paints.

### Solvent based paints

Many modern gloss paints are solvent based. These can contain up to 50% solvents and VOCs and can have serious health effects. High gloss paints, some specialist paints and aerosols usually contain the highest levels of VOCs.

### Natural paints

These are made from plant and mineral bases. Some are odourless and contain no solvents or VOCs at all, and are harmless to people and the environment. If your local DIY shop cannot get them, you can buy them by mail order. Two sources you could try are Ecos paints from Lakeland Paints, telephone 01539 732866 and Livos products from the Nature Maid Company, telephone 01952 883288.

## Wood and Forest Products

One important message of this book is that natural products are preferable to synthetic ones. However, most wood used in this country in DIY materials is imported, and in the past it was impossible to know whether the wood and wood products we bought were taken from sustainable sources or virgin forests. It is often assumed that softwoods are OK and hardwoods are not. In reality, the situation is more complicated than this; northern forests can be just as much at risk as tropical ones.

It is now possible to identify forest products which have been sustainably produced. Products certified by the Forest Stewardship Council have been independently assessed according to strict social, environmental and economic standards. Look for this label not only on timber itself, but on all products containing wood, including flooring, wallpapers, MDF and charcoal.

Alternatively, seek out reclaimed wood from specialist dealers or builders. This way you can enjoy the benefits of well-seasoned timber at no cost to the environment. You may find that it is cheaper too.

**Deforestation**

Some poor countries in the tropics have welcomed loggers who can get a good price from the West for quality hardwoods. Vast areas of forests have been destroyed, either for wood or to use the land to farm. Erosion of the shallow soil makes the land unusable within a few years. Because the forests are clear felled, they do not regenerate. As a result:

- The flora and fauna of the rainforests is lost for ever – it is possible that some species have become extinct before they have even been discovered.

- The greenhouse effect (see Global Warming, chapter 8) is aggravated because hundreds of square miles of trees which turn carbon dioxide into oxygen are felled.

- The release of carbon dioxide from burning the land to clear it after felling also contributes to global warming via the greenhouse effect.

## Protecting Woodwork

Wood preservatives are designed to protect the wood from insects and fungi. Modern chemical preservatives contain potent poisons which are effective and long lasting. Unfortunately, the chemicals which poison the insects and fungi are not likely to do human beings much good either. They give off VOCs and are difficult to dispose of safely. There are alternatives:

- Use well seasoned timber in the first place.

- Always protect timber from damp.

- Paint or varnish exposed wood and use beeswax polish on furniture.

- If you do need to treat timber against insect or fungal attack, use a wood protection agent based on natural substances, such as borax.

- If you have a serious problem, there are companies specialising in preserving wood by environmentally friendly methods.
- If you do use chemical wood preservatives, do not dispose of them down the drains where they will pollute the water supply.

## Decorating Your Home

Some people seem to re-decorate their homes as a form of entertainment. This is a complete mystery to most of us as it involves a great deal of hard work, mess and disruption! It also uses up resources and is a form of unnecessary consumption. There are many TV programmes and magazine articles encouraging us to redesign and re-decorate our homes frequently to keep up with the latest fashions. Everyone wants to have a nice home and we all like a change from time to time, but there really is no need to change the decorations inside the house every couple of years.

When you do come to change your décor, consider the potential effects on your health and the environment as well as appearances. It can be useful to try your own Life Cycle Analysis (see below) of the products you use. Floor coverings and furniture made from natural materials are much less likely to give off harmful chemicals than synthetic carpets and veneered particle-board furniture. A lot of the decorating materials advertised by manufacturers and promoted by magazine and television 'experts' are made from synthetic materials and plastics. Ask yourself whether you really want to surround yourself with these. As well as being easier on your health, natural materials are likely to have a much less detrimental effect on the environment during their manufacture and are easier to dispose of safely at the end of their useful life.

### Life Cycle Analysis

Life Cycle Analysis (LCA) involves the analysis of the environmental impact of a product at every stage of its life. It starts with the manufacture of the product, and ends with its disposal.

Factors considered include:

- Whether the raw materials are renewable
- What environmental costs are involved in obtaining the raw materials
- The environmental impact of the manufacturing process
- Pollution caused during the useful life of the product
- Environmental problems created by disposal.

## *Ventilation*

If you are using particleboard, plastic foams, glues, synthetic materials, cleaners, paints or anything else you think may give off VOCs, ensure that the room is well ventilated while you are working. Modern double-glazing is very good at keeping out the cold, but it also keeps out the fresh air. If possible, do any such jobs in the warmer months, when you can keep the windows open for longer, and drying times are shorter.

## *Resisting Gadgets*

It is possible to buy special tools for almost every job. Some of these do make the job easier and safer – an electric drill for example is virtually essential for some jobs. But only a few tools are necessary for basic home maintenance.

For example, a sponge, a scraper and some warm soapy water is perfectly adequate for stripping most wallpaper. However, retailers may try to convince you that you need a special stripping solution or even an electrically operated steam wallpaper stripper. Unless you live in a stately home, this is probably unnecessary!

Be aware, however, that for your safety's sake, special equipment is necessary for some jobs. For example, for high level work it is much safer to hire scaffolding rather than trying to make do with ladders. Always be guided by your common sense.

Many gadgets run on batteries or mains electricity, using power and creating noise, and unless you know what you are doing some can be very dangerous. Don't be seduced by advertising – most gadgets end up forgotten in a corner of the garage or shed.

## Action Points

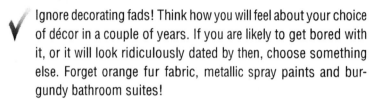

Ignore decorating fads! Think how you will feel about your choice of décor in a couple of years. If you are likely to get bored with it, or it will look ridiculously dated by then, choose something else. Forget orange fur fabric, metallic spray paints and burgundy bathroom suites!

Try to minimise the number of chemicals in your home. Ask questions about what you are buying. Choose a natural substitute whenever possible.

Always read the labels, particularly with regard to your own (and your family's) safety, and the safe disposal of the product.

Take particular care not to expose children to VOCs. Developing children are more sensitive to toxic chemicals than adults. Why experiment with children's health? For the same reason, try to avoid exposure to VOCs if you are pregnant.

Try to get in the habit of thinking about the environmental impact of your purchases before you make them. Remember the Life Cycle Analysis.

Look for the Forest Stewardship Council mark on wood products.

Use recycled and second-hand materials whenever possible.

If you need to use power tools, investigate the possibilities of hiring them, or sharing with family and friends, before you buy one for your sole use.

Buy only the quantity of materials you need for a particular job, unless you know you will be using them soon. Don't buy in bulk because it seems cheaper – the chances are the remainder will just sit on the shelf for years.

✔ Use your power as a consumer to encourage retailers to stock environmentally friendly products and sell things in small quantities when required.

## Summing Up

DIY is a difficult area for people wishing to adopt a greener lifestyle. Many widely available DIY materials contain some very unpleasant chemicals indeed and it makes sense to protect your health and the environment by minimising your use of them. Try to achieve a balance between properly maintaining your home and giving into commercialism.

We need to make our concerns about health and environmental damage known to government and manufacturers. Only if we do this will they put more effort into developing less harmful products. For ideas about how to do this see Chapter 12.

## Chapter 8

# Get Switched On

Meeting the world's energy needs will be one of the greatest challenges of the new century.

In the developed world power is relatively cheap and we take it for granted. Our demands are insatiable. More and more everyday tasks are now done by machine which a generation ago would have been done by hand. In our kitchens we have dishwashers, electric carving knives, juicers, bread makers, and food processors. In our gardens, we drive each other mad every Sunday afternoon by the constant noise of mowers, strimmers and hedge trimmers. Our children have battery- operated toys, televisions and computers in their bedrooms.

However, this *does* mean that as individuals most of us have a good deal of scope to reduce the amount of power we use, to the benefit of our wallets as well as the environment. In this chapter we will be explaining the problems and looking at ways of saving energy in your home by making the best use of:

- Insulation
- Heating
- Lighting
- Appliances.

We will also look at new opportunities to use your purchasing power to support companies which produce 'green' energy.

# The Real Costs of Energy

The price of energy in financial terms is relatively low. In environmental terms the costs are enormous:

- Resources are finite and diminishing. It has taken millions of years for deposits of oil, coal and gas to form, but we are using them up very quickly. It's not a question of *whether* they run out, but *when*.

- When fossil fuels are burned, they release carbon dioxide into the atmosphere. This causes global warming (see below). According to the Department of the Environment, the energy used by the average home creates 7 tonnes of carbon dioxide a year.

- Power stations release sulphur dioxide and nitrogen oxide into the atmosphere, causing acid rain.

### Acid Rain

Sulphur dioxide and nitrogen oxides from power stations and car emissions mix in the atmosphere with water vapour and oxygen to form sulphuric acid and nitric acid. These eventually fall back to earth as 'acid rain', possibly hundreds of miles away from the original source. Acid rain kills forests and pollutes lakes. Some lakes in the UK are 'dead' and the fish in others are threatened.

- There are significant environmental costs in extracting and transporting fuel. Landscapes are scarred by mining and seas are polluted by oil spills.

- Nuclear fuel was hailed as the clean and cheap energy source of the future. However, the costs are incalculable in terms of risk of accidental release of radiation and the difficulty of disposing of nuclear waste. Despite the fact that this problem of waste disposal has never been solved we continue to produce more and more of it. The fact that radioactivity cannot be seen makes it potentially all the more dangerous. This is one form of pollution which lasts forever.

- Even so called green energy can have massive environmental costs if it's not done properly. For example the Cardiff bay barrage (harnessing wave power) has involved flooding a huge area of mudflats which was an important feeding area for migrant birds.

### Global Warming

Carbon dioxide and other gases in the atmosphere act as a global 'greenhouse', warming the earth. Climate change:

- is causing the polar ice caps to melt, leading to a rise in sea levels and extensive flooding

- is causing increasingly extreme and dangerous weather conditions. In the future, dry regions are likely to get dryer and wet regions wetter. Floods and drought will become more common and more devastating.

- will lead to more and more people being driven from their homes as a result of environmental devastation. Some environmentalists estimate that by the middle of this century 150 million people are likely to be displaced because of extreme weather.

- affects plants and animals. For example, global warming is thought to contribute to the poor breeding success of cod in British waters.

- is causing serious diseases such as malaria to spread beyond the tropics.

# Insulation

One of the most important ways you can reduce carbon dioxide emissions is to insulate your home, saving money as well as energy. However, energy efficiency does not mean that it is necessary to seal your home; ventilation is important too. If you have a solid fuel fire or gas appliances ventilation is essential. A heating engineer will be able to advise you as to what is necessary. It is particularly important to have good ventilation in your kitchen and bathroom to prevent condensation. Here are some suggestions for improving the insulation in your home:

- **Loft insulation** - This is is one of the most effective ways of insulating your home. It should be at least 6" thick. This can cut your heating bills by about 20%.

- **Wall insulation** - More heat is lost through walls than any other way, so it is worth considering insulating them. If your home was built after 1930, it probably has cavity walls, and insulating them is relatively straightforward. This has to be done by a professional installer, and can be done in a day. Make sure it is installed by a member of the Cavity Wall Insulation Guarantee Agency (CIGA) who will give you a 25 year guarantee. Different types of insulating material are used. Before any installation, make sure you find out exactly what materials will be used and whether they emit VOCs. Insulating solid walls is more difficult and expensive, but may be worth investigating.

- **Wrapping up** - Take a look at your hot water cylinder. Modern ones come with built in insulation. Installing a ready made jacket on an old cylinder is a very easy and cheap job and will keep your water hot for longer as well as saving you money. If you have an old cylinder jacket which is falling to bits, replace it!

- **Double glazing** - According to the Energy Saving Trust, up to 23% of the heat lost from your home is through windows. Double glazing can reduce this by half. New energy efficient glass, called low emissivity glass, can reduce the heat loss by a further 10%. If you can't afford double glazing, thick curtains with thermal linings will help. Close all curtains at dusk to prevent heat escaping.

- **Draught proofing** - This is easy and cheap to do. Draughts around windows, doors and floors can mean the loss of around a fifth of the heat in the house. DIY draught proofing materials for doors and windows are widely available. If you have draughts between the floor and the skirting boards, this is easily cured with wooden beading. Train your family to close doors behind them – even if they are only nipping out for a moment. (We're still working on ours!)

## Heating

We live in a cool part of the globe and it is important to keep warm, especially if you are elderly, disabled or have young children. However, it is possible to be warm and comfortable and still save energy. You can do this by making sure that you have the heat when and where you want it.

- It is frequently suggested that if you have central heating you can reduce your heating bills by 10% by turning your thermostat down just 1°C. (I recommend that you also wear a thicker sweater! - Ann)

- The rooms you live in need to be warmer than the rest of the house. If you have central heating, you can fit thermostatic radiator valves to regulate the temperature in particular rooms. Our solution is to keep the central heating low, and to have a fire in the living room.

- Make sure you fully understand how to use your central heating controls, and make sure that the heating is only on when you need it. Turn it down or off when you go out.

- Don't have your domestic water scalding hot. This is dangerous and wasteful. If you have a cylinder thermostat, it is usually recommended that you set it at about 60°C.

- You can buy reflective material from DIY stores to stick behind radiators to reflect heat back into the room. You can also fit small shelves about two inches (five centimetres) above radiators to guide heat into the room.

- Have boilers and gas fires serviced regularly, both from the point of view of safety and efficiency.

- New types of boilers, particularly oil or gas fired condensing ones, are much more efficient than older models. Although these are expensive, they can save you over £100 a year in heating costs.

**DIY Green Energy**

Even in this country, it is possible to heat water by using solar panels. A one kilowatt solar panel can save a tonne of carbon dioxide emissions every year. Wind turbines are another source of 'free' energy if you live in a suitable place. For more information contact the Solar Energy Society, or the National Energy Foundation.

## Lighting

Good lighting is important for your comfort and safety. Here are some suggestions for saving energy:

- Switch lights off when you leave a room.
- Fit low-energy light bulbs, especially where lights are left on for long periods.
- Choose light fittings and shades which give a good light.
- Use task lighting as well as background lighting. Lamps can be placed to shine the light exactly where you need it.
- Light coloured walls reflect light, and reduce the need for high-wattage bulbs.
- Make the best use of daylight by pulling curtains well back, opening blinds and not obscuring windows with furniture.
- Fluorescent bulbs are far more efficient than ordinary light bulbs and may be appropriate in some parts of your home. Switching a fluorescent bulb on and off frequently is likely to reduce its lifespan. The Energy Efficiency Advice Centre suggests switching off if you are leaving a room for ten minutes or more.

# Appliances

If you are choosing new appliances, take into account their energy efficiency as this varies considerably from model to model. By law, the European Community Energy Label must be displayed on new refrigerators, freezers, washing machines and tumble dryers. The scheme will eventually also cover dishwashers, light bulbs and other appliances. Some washing machines and light bulbs have also been awarded the European Ecolabel (see Chapter 5).

Before buying new appliances, think carefully about whether you need them. You may be able to afford a dishwasher, but do you really need one? They use additional power and water and you need more crockery.

## *Ten ways to use appliances wisely*

1 Dry washing outside if possible, rather than using a tumble dryer

2 Make sure you have a full load before using washing machines and dishwashers

3 Use your washing machine on a low temperature programme unless the clothes are very dirty

4 Don't fill the kettle; just boil the amount of water you need and if you live in a hard water area, keep your kettle descaled

5 Don't put the fridge next to the cooker or a radiator or in a sunny place

6 Avoid leaving the fridge door open for longer than necessary

7 Avoid putting hot food in the fridge; let it cool down first

8 Defrost your fridge and freezer regularly

9 Switch televisions off at the set, rather than using the remote control

10 Use a shower (but not a power shower) rather than taking a bath

## Choosing Your Electricity Supplier

You now have a choice of electricity supplier. It *does* matter which supplier you choose, as they all perform very differently in terms of how green they are. You can obtain a free leaflet, 'Guide to Buying Green Energy' from Friends of the Earth Publications Despatch, or look on their informative and user-friendly website for up-to-date information.

There are currently two electricity companies which only supply green energy. They do this by supplying electricity from renewable sources to the national grid, and undertake to supply enough to cover the power used by their customers.

## Action Points

 Try to interest your children in toys which don't rely on batteries.

 Call Energy Efficiency, an initiative of the Energy Saving Trust, for details of free home energy checks. Energy Efficiency Advice Centres can also give free independent advice on cutting fuel bills.

 If you are in receipt of benefits or aged 60 or over you may be entitled to a Home Energy Efficiency Scheme grant. These can help with loft insulation, draught proofing outside doors and windows, cavity wall insulation (if you already have loft insulation) or upgrading heating controls. For more details, write to the Energy Action Grants Agency.

 Carry out an inspection of your home with a view to improving insulation. You can find out how much each measure will cost and what the annual savings will be by contacting the Energy Saving Trust.

 Look at the section on heating and set yourself a target to reduce your bills over the coming year.

Consider what you can do in your own home to improve the efficiency of your lighting.

Go through the list of ways to use appliances wisely. Decide which you can do and try and think of some other ideas for yourself.

✓ Train yourself and your family to close doors and turn off lights!

## Summing Up

We *must* call a halt to our ever increasing demands for energy. We can all make *some* changes. Remember that a lot of this is simply to do with habit and developing greener ways of thinking.

It is easy to ignore the connections between what we do in our own homes and wider issues such as global warming and acid rain. However, there are well-established direct causal links which we can't afford to ignore. The effects are beginning to be felt now: our weather is changing, sea levels are rising, forests and lakes are dying. The implications for the not too distant future are enormous. Are we to be judged as the generation which didn't care?

## Chapter 9

# Travel

Travel is something we take for granted. Despite the frustrations of overcrowding and congestion we are by far the most mobile generation ever.

This chapter follows on directly from the previous one. The message is much the same. Just as many of us have the money to squander electricity, we can also buy cheap tickets and hop on a plane to Paris for the weekend. But in environmental terms, we cannot afford to go on doing this. We believe that, as individuals, we all share responsibility for the future of the planet. The way you can demonstrate your own commitment is by showing some restraint yourself and by taking action in support of greener and fairer transport systems.

## The Mobile Society

We have created a whole society based on cheap road transport. In some ways this has given us valuable freedom and great social, educational, leisure and economic choices. People do have greater opportunities to mix and understand each other.

However, the fact that it *is* so cheap has hugely increased the opportunities for unnecessary journeys. We can now choose to live long distances from work and commute daily. We think nothing of driving fifty miles for a day's shopping.

Cheap transport has tended to undermine the individuality of local communities. It has meant the loss of many local shops and industries which have been unable to compete with national and international companies who can bring in goods at low cost. We transport basic foodstuffs up and down the country by lorry – lorries full of butter travelling North passing lorries full of butter travelling South. This reflects the increased globalisation of trade and the concentration of economic power into the hands of multinational businesses.

## Counting the Costs of Travel

As a society, we're only just beginning to recognise the true environmental and social costs of our addiction to travel. Road transport in the UK is responsible for:

- 48% of nitrogen oxides emitted. These contribute to acid rain (See Chapter 8)
- 28% of particulates or soot, which are linked to respiratory problems and heart disease.
- 20% of emissions of carbon dioxide, leading to global warming (See Chapter 8).
- High levels of noise pollution
- The costs and frustration resulting from congestion
- Vast areas of the countryside being covered in tarmac, and the associated destruction of wildlife and habitats including many Sites of Special Scientific Interest (SSSIs).
- The ruin of landscapes by road building
- Increased development in sensitive areas (eg National Parks) as a result of new roads
- Road accidents which killed 3,599 people in the UK in 1997
- Limits to the freedom of children, who are often kept indoors because of the danger from traffic. In 1997, 171 children were killed and 4,799 seriously injured while walking or cycling.

- The demise of small, independent shops in villages and town centres as people drive to out-of-town shopping centres.
- The social exclusion of non-drivers, particularly older people and less affluent families.

## The Car Culture

Whether we like it or not, our society is dominated by the car. And even with greatly improved public transport, a lot of people would be reluctant to give up their cars. We know as well as you do how pleasant it is to get into a warm car and go wherever you want! Even taking into account worsening traffic congestion and recent increases in the price of petrol, cars are still extremely convenient and relatively cheap.

Sadly, for some people, a car is a vital prop for their self-image. Advertisers, of course, are well aware of this, and play on it by emphasising the potency and glamour of the particular model they're trying to sell. This concentration on speed and machismo then leads the more susceptible to drive aggressively, wasting fuel and causing accidents. Perhaps one day, we will grow up and driving powerful cars aggressively will be seen as irresponsible rather than glamorous.

We all need to show restraint in car use, and use them only for essential journeys, rather than habitually driving everywhere without a second thought.

### *Being a greener car owner*

- Drive a smaller car. Don't be seduced into buying a larger car than you need.
- Keep it well maintained.
- Learn to drive carefully with regard to fuel consumption – reduce speed and do not accelerate or brake unnecessarily. See your car manual for more information on saving fuel.
- All newer cars have catalytic converters and use lead free petrol. If you have an older car, investigate the possibility of converting it.

- Don't have unnecessary gadgets on your car. Extras such as four wheel drive, electric windows, air conditioning and CD players all increase fuel consumption. If your car already has them, use them as little as possible.
- Before you open your car door, ask yourself if you could walk, cycle or use public transport instead.
- Avoid short journeys; your car is least efficient and causes most pollution during the first two miles of any journey.
- If you make a regular journey, for example to work or shop, consider whether it is possible to share transport with a colleague or neighbour. If you have access to the Internet, you can offer lifts through Freewheelers (see Action Points).
- Organise your life so that you can manage with one car in the household. Having two cars doubles the resources used in manufacture and inevitably increases car use.
- Join a breakdown service which does not campaign for more road building.

## Public Transport

Carrying large numbers of people in a train or a bus causes much less pollution than if those individuals all travelled separately by car.

Because public transport gets such a bad press, we tend to overlook its advantages to us as well as the environment. Even allowing for the delays in an under resourced network, it is still much safer and more relaxing to travel by train or bus. You can read a book or look at the passing countryside without having to worry about traffic.

Unfortunately, because we assume that using public transport is not practical, a lot of the time we don't even investigate the possibilities. If everyone making a journey enquired about bus and train services, perhaps the operators would become aware of increased demand and put on more services. At present, we're not creating a demand, so we don't get the services.

 **Why we don't need more roads**

For decades we have been trying to solve our traffic congestion problems by building more roads. Throughout this period, environmentalists have consistently argued that building new roads simply generates more traffic and at last this argument seems to be gaining acceptance. However, there is still a powerful road building lobby which loses no opportunity to press for more roads. Building new roads always brings new development, in turn generating more traffic. The only sensible way to solve the congestion problem is to reduce our reliance on cars and lorries.

We can do this as individuals (see below) but it also requires a radical re-think of the way commerce is organised and goods are moved around the country.

### *Reducing your need to travel*

Most of the time, we don't have much choice about how much time we spend travelling, although we may be able to choose the mode of transport. However, when looking for a job or moving house, we have the opportunity to radically improve our lives by taking into account travel arrangements:

- Live near where you work
- Live near a railway or bus route
- Investigate the possibilities of working from home – new technology is making this feasible for increased numbers of people
- Choose a local school for your children – if you don't like it, can you help to improve it?

## Global Travel and Tourism

Global travel has become part of life. Forty-eight weeks of the year become bearable with a fortnight's skiing in winter and two weeks in the sun in summer. But air travel is massively polluting, and tourism often brings economic benefits to the tour company, but only environmental degradation and increased squalor to the host country.

## The costs of air travel

Both the United Nations and the UK government acknowledge that aeroplanes are a serious threat to the environment. Aeroplanes are responsible for 3.5% of man-made global warming today, and there are fears that this will increase to 15% in the next fifty years. As well as carbon dioxide, aircraft engines also emit sulphur and nitrogen dioxides (contributing to acid rain). As the number of people flying grows, no amount of increased efficiency in engines or other improvements will stop this trend.

Friends of the Earth has urged governments to use taxation to encourage people to switch from aeroplanes to trains for short distances. At present, airlines pay no duty for fuel – unlike car drivers, for whom around two thirds of the price of petrol is duty and VAT. Nor is there any VAT on the price of air tickets or the cost of new airliners.

The expansion of airports to meet increasing demand for air travel is also a major cause of pollution and environmental damage. This is not only a problem in terms of the obvious effects of putting yet more acres under tarmac and further increasing noise pollution, it also creates more traffic congestion and involves the building of yet more roads.

### Food miles

The concept of food miles helps us to remember the environmental cost of buying food from across the globe. Buying French beans from Kenya and strawberries from the USA may be a treat, but carrying food by air is an outrageous waste of resources and causes massive amounts of pollution for nothing more than a luxury. Think of the cost in food miles as well as the price you have to pay.

## Tourism and developing countries

Tourism is the world's largest industry, but it doesn't always benefit people living in the countries we visit. Most holidaymakers would be horrified to think that they were taking water, land and food from local people when they stay in their hotel in the sun, or that rare turtles may become extinct because they can no longer breed on the beaches due to disturbance. Of course, these things are not mentioned in the holiday brochure!

To go on holiday with a clear conscience, find out about the environmental stance of the holiday companies you are considering booking with. Read their brochures carefully and ask awkward questions. Some specialist tour companies work with local communities to enable them to benefit from tourism without exploiting them or the environment.

When you get to your holiday destination, treat the local environment as you would like people to treat your own:

- Don't waste scarce resources, such as water and energy
- Buy gifts and souvenirs from local craftspeople, but not if they are made from shells or other endangered species
- Respect local environments; don't pick wild flowers or cause damage to fragile habitats such as coral
- Don't create litter – waste disposal is a major problem in some countries
- Stay in locally owned hotels if you can
- Respect local cultures and traditions.

### Biodiversity

Biodiversity describes the amazing number of different species of plants and animals on the planet. Extinction is worrying, not only because different species are interesting, attractive and useful to us, but also because all life is interdependent: The fewer species there are, the harder it is for the rest to survive. The current generation will see the extinction of between a third and a half of the world's species due to pollution and loss of habitat.

## Action Points

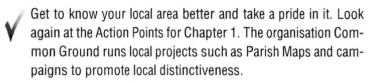

Get to know your local area better and take a pride in it. Look again at the Action Points for Chapter 1. The organisation Common Ground runs local projects such as Parish Maps and campaigns to promote local distinctiveness.

Take an interest in local planning decisions and challenge the need for more road building.

Lobby your local councils to introduce measures favouring walkers and cyclists rather than cars and lorries, such as traffic calming schemes.

Complain to the Advertising Standards Authority about car adverts which encourage fast or aggressive driving. Contact them for their specific rules concerning motoring advertisements. Queries can be answered over the phone, but specific complaints need to be made in writing.

For complaints about broadcast adverts, contact the Independent Television Commission.

Consider whether you might be better off hiring a car when you really need one instead of owning one.

Investigate car-sharing. Freewheelers is a free Internet based service linking drivers and passengers to share the cost of travel. Contact them to offer or request lifts.

Lobby politicians for better public transport facilities – see Chapter 12.

Consider the health benefits of walking and cycling.

Reduce your shopping trips. An increasing number of items can now be bought via mail order or the Internet.

Contact Tourism Concern for more information about sustainable tourism. They produce a directory of eco-friendly holidays.

If your life is only made bearable by the thought of your next holiday abroad, you really do need to reconsider your lifestyle! See Chapter 1 and Chapter 11 for more thoughts on this.

## Summing Up

Transport and travel is one of the most challenging issues for green campaigners. Our whole society revolves around the car, and life can be difficult for non-car owners. Any changes you can make will depend very much on where you live and on your own individual circumstances, but we can all campaign for a better public transport system and less dependence on the car.

Ideally, we should take into account the issues raised in this chapter in our every day lives. At certain times, particularly when we choose a place to live, look for a new job or take a holiday, they become even more important.

## Chapter 10

# Looking Good

Having acted on all the previous chapters, you should be looking good already! You will be eating healthy food and taking lots of exercise and living in a less polluted environment.

But for most of us, looking good is more than that. It's about our clothes, our hair and the cosmetics and toiletries we use; the signals we send out through our appearance about who we are and what we stand for.

This chapter looks at the major environmental and human issues surrounding the fashion and cosmetics industries. We give suggestions to help you look good without damaging the environment or exploiting people or animals.

## A Change of Clothing

Everybody knows that the fashion industry depends on constant change. And it's not just the young and trendy who are influenced by this - no-one wants to look as though they are stuck in a time warp. The influence of fashion seems to creep up on us without us knowing why. Suddenly, the cut of those trousers or the colour of that jacket is embarrassing, even though we have no interest whatsoever in what is happening on the catwalk.

Whether we like it or not, we are judged by our appearance, and it can be very difficult to resist the pressure to keep up to date. As a result, most of us have wardrobes full of clothes we never wear and don't know what to do with. The more ruthless have a clearout every now and then and take it all down to the charity shop.

The answer to this is to have one last sort out. And then adopt the fashion guru's mantra: 'less is more'. Whatever your income, it makes sense to buy fewer, but better quality clothes on which you can base your wardrobe. Unfortunate though this may be for the extroverts among us, the less striking the garment, or outrageous the colour, the more often you will be able to wear it, and you will be able to wear it for longer before it looks out of date. Whether you are male or female, you can express your individuality and fashion sense with the way you wear your clothes and your choice of accessories.

Happily, this makes sense in environmental as well as fashion terms. It is also a golden opportunity to get rid of clutter and simplify your life. Instead of having a wardrobe jammed with out of date clothes you can have a few outfits which you know will look good anywhere. This makes deciding what to wear a great deal easier and will also save you money in the long run.

### Liz's story

Liz worked in the centre of a busy town, and usually spent her lunch hour walking round the shops. She found clothes hard to resist and easily spent two or three hundred pounds a month on them. 'When I started saving for a deposit on a house, I was surprised to find just how much I was spending,' says Liz. 'I needed to find something to keep me away from the shops in my lunch hour.' She found the perfect solution by joining a local gym, where the subscription was only thirty pounds a month. 'After six months at the gym, I now get more compliments on my appearance than when I had a wardrobe full of clothes,' she says.

# Artificial Versus Natural Fabrics

We used to think that if we bought natural fabrics, we would be buying environmentally friendly clothing, because it was made from renewable resources and would biodegrade. However, natural fabrics also have an environmental cost. The list below looks at some of the most popular clothing fabrics and any environmental problems associated with their manufacture.

- **Polyester and nylon** - Man-made fabrics, such as polyester and nylon are made from non-renewable petrochemicals. Manufacturing them uses large amounts of water and energy and the fabric is not biodegradable. This is a chemical industry causing large-scale pollution.

- **Cotton** - Almost all cotton is produced with little regard for the environment. Cotton is already one of the most heavily sprayed crops in the world. Even more worrying is the fact that genetically modified cotton has now been developed in the USA to withstand even greater amounts of pesticides. Organic cotton is slowly coming onto the market, but at present few mainstream outlets stock clothing made from organically grown cotton and it can be expensive. However, as more people become aware of the damaging effects of conventional cotton growing, more companies are looking to use organic cotton. You can buy organic cotton clothing from Natural Collection and various environmental organisations. Patagonia, an outdoor clothing company, uses 100% organic cotton, and some major manufacturers use small amounts of organic cotton and blend it with conventional cotton.

- **Wool** - The main problem with wool production is the chemicals in sheep dip which poison workers and leach out of the fleece when it is washed and get into the water supply.

- **Viscose and Rayon** - These fabrics are made from cellulose from wood pulp. Caustic soda or acids are used in the manufacturing process and these are then discharged into water systems.

- **Linen** - Linen is made from the fibre of the flax plant. Flax is not so heavily sprayed as cotton, and less water is used in the manufacture of linen than cotton, but there still may be problems with dyes and bleaching agents used (see below).

- **Silk** - Silk is produced from silk moth caterpillars which are killed in order to obtain the silk. Silk moths are a domesticated insect which are thought not to exist in the wild. It takes around 5,500 silkworms to produce 1kg of raw silk. Vegans will not wear silk because they object to this slaughter.

- **Hemp** - The Body Shop and some fashion designers are leading a campaign to legalise the growing of hemp in the USA for making fabric, cosmetics and paper. Hemp makes strong, soft cloth, is a renewable resource, is biodegradable and does not need bleaching. Unfortunately, because hemp is related to cannabis, it is illegal to grow it in the USA.

- **Recycled fabrics** - Some polyester fleece fabric is made from recycled plastic bottles. This seems to be an excellent way of recycling bottles, but check on the label whether the fleece you are buying *is* recycled.

### Fabric dyes

Nearly all our clothes are bleached or dyed. This part of the manufacturing process is often the most polluting, regardless of the fabric used, with chemical residues ending up in water courses, affecting fish and plant life. Look for clothes made with natural dyes. Organic cotton clothing is generally unbleached or uses environmentally friendly dyes.

## Looking Good and Feeling Good Too

It can come as a shock to realise how damaging the clothing industry is. But one of the messages of this book is that if you have the information, you can take action in a practical way. Apply the Life Cycle Analysis to your purchases (see Chapter 7), and look in the

Action Points for more guidance about how to look good *and feel good* about what you are wearing.

## How Fair is What You Wear?

Little clothing is made nowadays in the UK. The reason for this is that labour is very cheap indeed in many developing countries. So cheap, in fact, that many people consider it to be slave labour. Poverty is so extreme in countries such as Taiwan, Bangladesh, Indonesia, India, Honduras, the Dominican Republic and the Philippines that even young children are forced to work. Many of these people (often women and children) work in appalling conditions for 15 hour days, seven days a week. In May 1996 Oxfam launched a campaign against sweatshops, calling on the UK's top retailers to accept responsibility for the treatment of workers producing their goods in developing countries.

### Ethical Trading

In 1998, the Ethical Trading Initiative (ETI) was launched. This comprises a network of companies, trade unions and non-governmental organisations, including Oxfam, Christian Aid and the Fairtrade Foundation, and is supported by the UK government. It has developed a Code of Conduct which members have to adopt. Under pressure from consumers, some major UK companies have joined the ETI. Member companies agree to give workers a living wage, comply with improved working conditions, avoid discrimination and avoid exploiting children.

## Cruelty to Animals

### *Fur and feathers*

The Royal Society for the Protection of Birds (RSPB) was started in 1889 by a group of ladies concerned about the use of ostrich feathers to make hats, which were high fashion at the time. Animals have always suffered at the hands of the fashion industry. Most fur nowadays is produced on fur farms rather than by hunting. But this does not mean that the animals do not suffer. Most are kept in intensive and insanitary conditions. Furthermore, mink which have escaped or been released from fur farms in the UK create havoc in the surrounding countryside, preying on native animals such as water voles.

### Animal testing

Animals are still used for testing in the cosmetics industry, although it was banned in the UK in 1998. The EU is considering imposing a similar ban. Imported products or ingredients may well have been tested on animals. Animal testing involves considerable cruelty, inflicting pain and suffering, often without any anaesthetics. If you wish to avoid products developed in this way, always check the labels.

In the past, nearly all ingredients used in personal care products were tested on animals. This means that any product using traditional ingredients will contain substances at one time tested on animals. You cannot avoid this. But you can avoid supporting manufacturers who continue to carry out animal testing.

## Cosmetics, Your Health and the Environment

Many cosmetics and perfumes are largely chemical cocktails. Some contain artificial musks, which contaminate the environment and accumulate in the body. Other chemicals to avoid which may be in cosmetic products are nonoxynol and nonylphenol ethoxylate, which can disrupt hormones. These may or may not be listed in the ingredients. The best thing is to seek out natural products and avoid nonessential perfumes.

Many cosmetics are sold by means of their elaborate packaging. Most of this is unnecessary, wastes resources, causes pollution during manufacture, cannot be reused or recycled and adds to the cost. Look for products with minimal packaging, which can be reused or recycled. The Body Shop sells a range of products in refillable bottles, and also recycles returned containers.

## Action Points

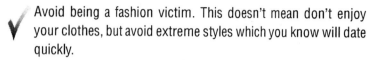

✓ Avoid being a fashion victim. This doesn't mean don't enjoy your clothes, but avoid extreme styles which you know will date quickly.

✓ Buy fewer clothes and cosmetics – don't be tempted to buy things you don't need just because they are cheap. Remember the environmental costs.

✓ Buy second-hand clothes. There are bargains to be had in charity shops and jumble sales. Some charities have shops specialising in designer and vintage clothes.

✓ Children grow out of clothes very quickly. Get together with friends and pass clothes and baby equipment around between you. Being green is not being mean!

✓ If they are in good condition, give clothes you have finished with to charity shops. Find out whether there are any facilities in your area for recycling clothes which are no longer wearable.

✓ Contact the Women's Environmental Network for their leaflets about clothes and the environment.

✓ Try to avoid clothes needing dry cleaning. Dry cleaning involves toxic solvents which continue to give off VOCs after you have brought the garment home.

✓ Choose your fabrics carefully. Buy organically produced cotton if you can. Look for clothes which use natural dyes. Check out the trading arms of environmental charities, and look at Ethical Consumer Magazine for more information.

✓ Lobby manufacturers to source green cotton and natural dyes. If enough people ask, they will find it!

✓ Write to manufacturers and retailers and ask them whether they are members of the Ethical Trading Initiative. Question what they know about the working conditions of the people who make their clothes. Ask if these are independently monitored. If they do not respond, do you really want to buy clothes from them?

Always look at the label when you are buying cosmetics and toiletries. Aim to buy cosmetics made from natural ingredients which have not been tested on animals.

Recycle packaging if you can.

## Summing Up

Not many generations ago, things were worn until they were worn out, and then cut down and the good parts made into children's clothes, patchwork quilts and even rag rugs. Nowadays we buy clothes for a season and then they're finished with. It is possible to enjoy wearing clothes without being wasteful.

There are environmental costs in making all new clothes, but you can avoid the worst offenders if you are willing to do your homework.

If you buy cosmetics and toiletries made from natural ingredients, they are likely to be better for you in the long run as well as kinder to the environment.

## Chapter 11

# Work and Money

This chapter looks at some of the wider issues surrounding work and money. It questions the prevailing ethos that we should all be maximising our earnings and aiming for the highest material standards. Reading this chapter you will be encouraged to think about what *you* consider to be a fulfilling lifestyle, and how you might move towards it.

## Looking at Your Lifestyle

We live in a society where money is equated with success. People are judged by their wealth and their job rather than their personal qualities. Unpaid activities such as looking after children, being a carer or doing voluntary work are undervalued. Part-time or low paid workers are seen as less important. Material success is the be all and end all of life.

This is not only a financial pressure. There is an expectation that people will be in paid employment, and women still apologetically confess to being 'only a housewife'. For men, even today, it is even more difficult for them to define themselves unless they have a regular job.

If you do have a highly paid job, you are expected to conspicuously consume in order to demonstrate your success to others.

### The altar of economic growth

Economic growth has been relentlessly pursued by governments regardless of social and environmental cost and we are constantly bombarded by advertising to consume more and more. The drive for economic growth has been extremely destructive and polluting and in the long term constant growth is not sustainable because resources are finite. We need to promote economic growth in environmentally sustainable ways.

### Leading a greener life

Leading a greener life is about consuming only what you need, and not being influenced by rampant commercialism. There is a misconception that being green is a luxury only the well to do can afford. In fact, well off people are less likely to be green because they usually consume more resources.

There is plenty of evidence that after a certain point has been reached, increasing our material possessions does not lead to happiness. As a society we need to get rid of our obsession with material standards, and promote quality of life for everyone instead.

There is little evidence that modern industrial society is ready for this, but many individuals are seeking something better in their lives. You don't *have* to accept the values of consumerism if you don't want to!

## Money, Work and Time

Increasing numbers of people are questioning whether they need to maintain their present standard of living. The concept of 'downshifting' has gained media attention in the past few years as some people have made the decision to accept lower earnings in exchange for a better quality of life.

To those who are struggling to maintain basic standards on a low income, this might seem like the self indulgence of the well to do, but there is a genuine green issue here. Choosing to spend less money and consume fewer resources benefits the environment.

# Spending to Your Limit

Wealth is relative and you need to decide for yourself what standard of living you aspire to.

Remember that you don't have to accept the standards of others. Conventional economic wisdom has it that you should take out the biggest mortgage you can afford and spend to your limit. Living in a smaller house, or perhaps driving a smaller car might put less stress on you as well as the environment. Spending less gives you the freedom to earn less.

## *Borrowing money*

Banks and other financial institutions are constantly pestering us with offers of loans and credit cards, usually at a high rate of interest. It can be quite difficult to resist the pressure, and positively inconvenient not to have a credit card (although a debit card is just as good for most transactions). This is all part of the pressure of commercialism, to make us spend more and consume more.

## *Credit unions*

Credit unions are co-operative, non-profit making associations usually based in a particular neighbourhood or workplace to enable members to save and borrow money usually in relatively small amounts. They are particularly helpful to people on low incomes or who do not have a bank account. They are local organisations, controlled by their members who buy an initial share and then after a period of regular savings are allowed to borrow money. They operate on the basis of meeting the needs of their members rather than on a commercial basis and interest rates are relatively low.

If you are interested contact the Association of British Credit Unions (ABCUL), or enquire at your local Citizens Advice Bureau.

### Lets Schemes

LETS stands for Local Exchange Trading Systems. Members exchange and share goods and services with each other. Tokens are used as a system of currency and no money changes hands. Each member offers the goods and services they can and by providing these builds up credit to buy from other members.

These are locally based and tend to build up community ties as well as being a cheap way of obtaining goods and services. Transport and specialist equipment such as DIY and gardening tools can be shared, helping to build a greener community.

For a list of main schemes and other information send a stamped addressed envelope to Letslink UK. Your local Citizens Advice Bureau should be able to tell you of any schemes operating locally.

## Ethical Investment

Most of us were brought up with the idea that saving is a 'good thing' and intrinsically virtuous. It may indeed be a good thing from the point of view of our own financial security, but generally speaking we give little thought to what banks and building societies do with our money. Many people would be horrified if they knew that their money was being used to invest in companies with interests in arms trading, nuclear power, tobacco production, oppressive regimes, environmentally damaging industries or animal testing.

The only way of being certain that your money is not used in these areas is to deal only with banks and other financial institutions who have clearly defined policies which make it clear which areas of investment they actively avoid.

### *Banks*

Although banks charge for their services, most of their money is made by lending money to individuals or companies. However, there are banks who will invest only in accordance with ethical criteria.

The Co-operative Bank has had an ethical and environmental policy since 1992. This takes into account such issues as human rights, armaments, trade and social involvement, ecological impact and animal welfare.

The Triodos Bank invests only in businesses which have positive environmental and social impacts, in such areas as renewable energy, organic food, fair trade and social housing. The bank informs customers through a newsletter of exactly which projects it finances. It offers the usual range of banking services.

## Building societies

Building societies were set up to provide mortgages to home buyers. They are owned by their borrowers and savers who are the members of the society. Since 1986, they have been allowed to raise up to 20% of their funds on the stock market.

A number of large former building societies have converted into banks over recent years. They are no longer owned by investors and borrowers, but by their shareholders, and can operate in exactly the same way as other banks.

The Ecology Building Society was formed in 1981 and has a positive environmental and ethical policy. It supports the restoration of older properties and environmentally friendly building projects. Members are regularly informed through newsletters about what projects it funds other than mortgages and about its lending policy to homebuyers.

## Shared Interest

Shared Interest is a co-operative lending society which helps workers in the developing world to establish environmentally friendly businesses by lending them money on fair terms. Anyone who invests money with them becomes a member of the society and has a say in the running of its affairs. If you are interested, contact the Shared Interest Society.

### Stock market investments

Most small investors on the stock market put their savings into unit trusts. Because unit trusts spread their risk by investing in a number of companies engaged in different activities, they are generally considered to be a safer investment than buying shares in individual companies. There has been a big growth in this area of investment and a number of companies now offer 'ethical' unit trusts.

A financial adviser with knowledge of ethical investments will be able to advise you on which trusts will best match your ethical concerns. A list of financial advisers with an interest in ethical investment can be obtained from the Ethical Investment Research Service (Eiris).

### Occupational pensions

From July 2000, occupational pension funds will be required to declare their environmental and ethical policies. If you are paying into an occupational pension scheme, you have the right to know how the money is being invested.

Occupational pensions schemes invest huge amounts of money and could be a significant influence in terms of raising ethical and environmental standards in major companies.

### Personal pensions

It is possible to buy personal pensions based on ethical investment. A number of companies have ethical funds. Financial advisers listed by Eiris can advise you.

### Insurance

Some insurance brokers also offer ethical household, travel and commercial insurance. Ask your broker whether they offer this service.

## Action Points

✓ Go back over the exercises in Chapter 1 and relate them to the discussion in this chapter. Are you in a position to make changes to your lifestyle?

✓ If you have spare money, put some in a local credit union.

✓ Find out if there is a LETS scheme in your area.

✓ Write to your bank and ask about their ethical and environmental policies. Keep asking questions.

✓ Consider transferring your current account to one of the banks we have mentioned.

✓ Consider transferring your savings to accounts and funds which operate in accordance with your principles.

✓ If you are a member of an occupational pension scheme, write and ask about their environmental and ethical policies. Try to encourage your pension scheme to act as a force for good by influencing the companies they invest in.

## Summing Up

Some major issues have been raised in this chapter. They are not to be taken lightly and will require a lot of further investigation and thought before you decide whether to make changes. All we have been able to do here is raise the issues, and give you pointers as to where to go for further information.

One thing that you can do now, regardless of your financial position, is to question the financial institutions you deal with about their ethical and environmental stance and try to persuade them to change it for the better. Remember that they are competing for your custom!

## Chapter 12

# Taking It Further

This chapter is for people who want to go further and take a more active part in reversing the destruction of our planet.

Much of this book has been about what you can do as an individual to lessen your impact on the environment, but for real change we need to influence politicians and companies. When enough people feel strongly about an issue, enormous pressure can be exerted. For example, so many people were incensed about having genetically modified foods forced on them by food manufacturers that the outcry persuaded supermarkets to go to a great deal of trouble to remove GMOs from their own brand foods.

In this chapter we will be talking about the steps you can take to put good intentions into practice.

## Organisations to Join

Joining relevant organisations is one of the best ways of keeping up to date with current issues. As well as providing financial support to them, it also gives them increased credibility. When the RSPB or the Ramblers take on a cause, it is that much more effective because of their huge memberships.

## General environmental organisations

- **Friends of the Earth** - If you are concerned about the issues in this book, the first thing that we recommend that you do is join Friends of the Earth. FOE is an established, responsible and well respected campaigning organisation. FOE spokespeople are often called on to comment on environmental issues in the national media, and they are effective at lobbying Parliament and organisations on green matters. They produce an informative and attractive magazine for supporters (Earth Matters), and have an equally useful website.

  As well as operating at a national level, FOE has local groups that campaign on national and local issues. You don't have to take part in these, but if you do it is an excellent way of meeting like minded people.

  FOE encourages its members to add their weight as individuals to national and local campaigns, and tells them how in very practical ways. Each issue of Earth Matters has a Take Action section, giving specific information about current issues and campaigns, who to write to and what other action to take.

- **Greenpeace** – Greenpeace is another organisation that campaigns and educates on a wide range of global environmental issues, including climate change, nuclear energy and the health of the oceans. They have run some very effective campaigns, raising the profile of important previously neglected issues with a great deal of imagination and panache.

## Other green organisations

There are many organisations that campaign on particular issues related to special interests. Some of the well-known ones are included in the listings at the back of the book. If you have a special interest, say in walking, cycling or natural history, you may want to join an organisation reflecting this.

Over the years, a number of these organisations have recognised the importance of environmental issues and the need for collective action to lobby decision makers. Many of them include in their magazines and newsletters specific action you can take, by changing your behaviour, writing letters and getting involved in group action.

## Lobbying for Change by Yourself

Writing letters can be a very effective way of getting across your point of view. Public relations is a major concern for all politicians, organisations and businesses. As well as wanting your approval in terms of votes or custom, they are very sensitive about bad publicity and will try to avoid this if they can.

You can write letters directly to the organisation or individual concerned, or to the local or national press and radio, or to your MP. Make sure you know who your MP is. You can find out at your local reference library. Write to them at the House of Commons, even if you think they will be unsympathetic to your point of view. Even if you do not get what you want, you will be helping to raise awareness and the profile of green issues generally (and you do receive a reply on smart paper in an impressive envelope!)

If you want to know more about the workings of Parliament, or to find out who your MP is, and you have access to the Internet, go to the United Kingdom Parliament website. One of the things you will find there is a list of ministers who are responsible for particular government departments. If for example, you are concerned about a food issue, you could write to the Minister responsible for Agriculture, Fisheries and Food. You need to find out their name and write to them personally.

### *Writing letters*

In order to make your letters effective, you may find the following guidelines helpful:

- Always write to a named individual in an organisation. If you are taking action on behalf of a pressure group, they will be able to tell you the name of the person you should write to. Otherwise, you can easily telephone the organisation in question and ask the name of the person in charge.

- Type your letters if possible, or print legibly – make them clear and easy to read.
- Pay attention to spelling and grammar.
- Keep them short and to the point – one typed sheet of A4 at the most.
- Write congratulatory letters as well as complaining ones.
- Make positive points as well as negative ones if you can – this makes your letter seem more thoughtful and balanced.
- Back up your arguments with facts and figures – but make sure that these are accurate.
- Don't make assumptions about what your readers will know. Always spell things out clearly.
- Make positive suggestions for change.
- Be polite. No matter how angry you are about something, being abusive will never get you anywhere. Your letter will go straight into the bin.
- Ask questions. If you are writing to a politician or an organisation, asking questions about what they plan to do makes it more difficult for them to dodge the issues in their reply.
- Always keep a copy of your letter.
- If you don't get a reply within a reasonable length of time, write again. A polite reminder of the date you wrote and the subject matter is all that is needed.

### Newspapers

If you keep an eye on the local press, you will often see stories and letters with environmental implications. Responding to these can raise awareness of green issues, help to shape public opinion and influence local politicians. This is probably your best chance to reach a wider audience.

One of us once wrote a letter to our local paper concerning the felling of a row of trees. We commented that Dorchester, our home town, had once been famous for its trees. We had the satisfaction of hearing that remark repeated many times by local politicians eager to associate their local knowledge and green credentials in the minds of the electorate.

## *Finding Facts*

We are often told we are living in 'the information age'. And so we are. But sometimes there can seem to be too much information, or you can find everything but what you want or need. Whatever the source of information, be aware of the possibility of bias. (Even we aren't completely objective all the time!)

Often campaigning groups already have the information you may need. Other important sources of information include:

- **The Internet** – The Internet is a wonderful source of information, once you get used to using it. But remember that anyone can put information on the net, and they don't necessarily all check their facts or present them in an objective way. Be discriminating about how you use the information you find there.

- **Quality newspapers** – These all have a particular political bias, but can be a vital source of up to date information.

- **Radio and television documentaries** – It is often in this form that a story breaks. Programme makers, however, also have their own agendas.

- **Books and magazines** –You don't have to buy these; they may be obtainable in your local library. Ethical Consumer magazine covers many important environmental issues in depth, and provides a good source of facts and figures you can use in your campaigning. The magazine includes comparative reports on the performance of different companies or products.

- **Companies** – Companies will often tell you quite a lot about what they are doing, either by providing PR material or by answering letters or telephone enquiries. But remember, most of the time it *is* a PR exercise.

- **Government organisations** – The Parliamentary website is a good starting point if you want to find out what government departments are doing.

# Local Action

People who organise local campaigns are often criticised as 'nimbies' – busybodies who are quite happy to see new roads built or dirty factories belching out filth so long as it is not causing them any inconvenience or affecting the value of their house. However, many of these campaigners are right, even if they are only prompted into action because it is a local issue. It is important to keep an eye on what is happening locally – if you don't, who will?

As well as the local press and the local council minutes, there are other ways of keeping yourself informed. Wildlife Trusts will be aware of local wildlife sites and developments threatening local habitats. You can find out which are the most likely sources of pollution in your area by looking at the 'Factory Watch' page on the FOE website. On the same website, there is a Wild Places page which lists any known threats to SSSIs (Sites of Special Scientific Interest).

## *Finding like-minded people*

It can be much more effective to campaign as a group rather than trying to do things on your own. If there is a relevant organisation, such as Friends of the Earth, the Ramblers or a Wildlife Trust, a good first step would be to contact them. You may find that there is already a local group you can join.

## *Organising a local campaign*

If you find that there are no local groups taking on the cause, you may wish to set up a local campaign yourself. The first step is to make sure you have your facts right. You are then in a position to get together with other interested people and decide as a group what you mean to achieve. You are more likely to achieve success if you offer a positive alternative rather than just opposition.

Identify the decision makers you will need to influence and the best way of influencing them. Decide whether you can achieve your aims by personal lobbying and writing letters or whether you need to set up a public meeting and publicise what you are doing.

Depending on the scale of your campaign, you might need to appoint people to take on key roles such as chairperson and secretary. If you need to raise money, you will need a treasurer. You should appoint a press officer who can be trusted to present your case accurately and consistently to journalists.

### *The public meeting*
If you do set up a public meeting, make sure it is carefully planned. A successful meeting will need:

- plenty of good publicity
- a suitable venue
- a clear agenda
- good speakers

An unsatisfactory meeting may be worse than nothing.

### *Involving the press*
Involving the press will provide you with free publicity. Make sure you give them an interesting story and, if possible, photo opportunities. Send the local papers and radio stations a press release giving brief details (no more than an A4 sheet) with the name and contact details of your spokesperson

### *Other tactics to consider:*
- **Letter writing** - ask people to write to the press, to politicians or to the company concerned.
- **A petition** – although generally these are less effective than individual letters.

- **Lobbying decision makers** – speak to local councillors and attend their surgeries.
- **Demonstrations**
- **Opposition to planning proposals**
- **Standing for local elections**
- **Leaflets and posters**

### *Campaign Guides*

Friends of the Earth publishes a series of campaign guides on specific topics like roads, housing developments and polluting factories. These can be purchased from their publications catalogue and some of them can be downloaded free from the online catalogue on their website.

## Volunteering

This can be a very practical way of helping the environment. Most organisations will welcome help with fundraising, clerical jobs, delivering newsletters and other basic tasks. Many of them depend on this to keep their costs as low as possible.

If you want to do something more physically demanding, you can volunteer for practical conservation work on local nature reserves. Contact your local Wildlife Trust, the RSPB or the British Trust for Conservation Volunteers.

If you find you enjoy this, you can spend your holidays doing it. The RSPB advertise regularly for volunteer wardens working for a week or more on some of their larger reserves.

## Action Points

 Join one or more environmental organisations.

Identify your interests. What issues do you feel most strongly about? Are these the areas that you could take further?

Identify what skills you have to offer. You may not want to seek the limelight, or have a great deal of time, but there is almost certainly something you can do. Try to think positively, rather than worrying about what you cannot do.

 Keep in touch with what is happening locally.

 Keep up to date with wider environmental issues. Read a quality newspaper. Learn to use the Internet. Many libraries now offer free access.

We hope that by now you are writing your own action points! Good luck.

## Summing Up

You may not see yourself as a natural campaigner, but you may be surprised by how much influence you *can* have. There are many things we can do as individuals to lessen our impact on the environment, but we also need to bring our influence to bear on decision makers if the difficulties facing the world are to be overcome. It can give enormous satisfaction to feel that you have done something to improve things.

Joining like-minded people will increase your confidence and effectiveness. As a member of an environmental organisation you will not only be supporting its work, but also helping to keep yourself well informed.

Showing by the way you live that people and the planet matter more to you than material possessions is wholly positive and life enhancing. It is as good for your psychological well-being as it is for your physical health - and good for the rest of the world as well.

If writing to charities and voluntary organisations for information, always enclose an SAE.

## Useful Organisations:

### Action Aid

Hamlyn House
Macdonald Road
Archway
London N19 5PG
Telephone: 020 7561 7561
E-mail: mail@actionaid.org.uk
Website: www.actionaid.org

### Advertising Standards Authority

2 Torrington Place
London WC1E 7HW
Telephone: 0171 580 5555
E-mail: via website below
Website: www.asa.org.uk

### Association of British Credit Unions Ltd (ABCUL)

Holyoake House
Hanover Street
Manchester M60 0AS
Telephone: 0161 832 3694
E-mail: info@abcul.org
Website: www.abcul.org

### British Trust for Conservation Volunteers

36 St Mary's Street
Wallingford
Oxfordshire OX10 0EU
Telephone: 01491 839766
E-mail: information@btcv.org.uk
Website: www.btcv.org

### British Union for the Abolition of Vivisection (BUAV)

16a Crane Grove
London N7 8LB
Telephone: 0171 700 4888

### Christian Aid

35 Lower Marsh
Waterloo
London SE1 7RT
Telephone: 0171 620 4444
E-mail: info@christian-aid.org
Website: www.christian-aid.org.uk

### Common Ground

PO Box 25309
London NW5 1ZA
Telephone: 0171 267 2144
E-mail: info@commonground.org.uk
Website: www.commonground.org.uk

### Compassion in World Farming

Charles House
5a Charles Street
Petersfield
Hants GU32 3EH
Telephone: 01730 264208 / 268863
E-mail: compassion@ciwf.co.uk
Website: www.ciwf.co.uk

## Cyclists Touring Club
Cotterell House
69 Meadrow
Godalming
Surrey GU7 3HS
Telephone: 01483 417217
E-mail: cycling@ctc.org.uk
Website: www.ctc.org.uk

## Energy Action Grants Agency
Freepost
PO Box ING
Newcastle Upon Tyne NE99 2RP
Telephone: 0800 072 0150

## Energy Saving Trust & Energy Efficiency Advice Centres
21 Dartmouth Street
London SW1H 9BP
Telephone: 0345 277 200
Telephone for details of your
local centre: 0800 512012
Website: www.est.org.uk

## Ethical Consumer Magazine
ECRA Publishing Ltd
Unit 21
41 Old Birley Street
Manchester M1 4EJ
Telephone: 0161 226 2929
Website: www.ethicalconsumer.org

## The Fairtrade Foundation
Suite 204
16 Baldwin's Gardens
London EC1N 7RJ
Telephone: 020 7405 5942
Website: www.fairtrade.org.uk

## The Food Commission UK Ltd
94 White Lion Street
London N1 9PF
Telephone: 020 7837 2250
E-mail:
foodcomm@compuserve.com
Website:
www.ourworld.compuserve.com/
homepages/foodcomm.htm

## Freewheelers
(An Internet only organisation)
E-mail:
Freewheelers@freewheelers.co.uk
Website: www.freewheelers.co.uk

## Friends of the Earth
26-28 Underwood Street
London N1 7JQ
Telephone: 0171 490 1555
E-mail: info@foe.co.uk
Website: www.foe.co.uk

## Friends of the Earth (Publications)
56-58 Alma Street
Luton LU1 2PH
Telephone: 0171 490 1555

## Furniture Recycling Network
Telephone: 0116 233 7007
E-mail: frn@btinternet.com

## Greenpeace UK
Canonbury Villas
London N1 2PN
Telephone: 0171 865 8100/ 8234
E-mail: gp-info@uk.greenpeace.org
Website: www.greenpeace.org

**Help the Aged**
St. James's Walk
Clerkenwell Green
London EC1R OBE
Telephone: 020 7253 0253

**Henry Doubleday Research Association (HDRA)**
Ryton on Dunsmore
Coventry CV8 3LG
Telephone: 01203 303517
E-mail: enquiry@hdra.org.uk
Website: www.hdra.org.uk

**Independent Television Commission**
33 Foley Street
London W1P 7LB
Telephone: 020 7255 3000

**Letslink UK**
2 Kent Street
Portsmouth
Hampshire PO1 3BS
Telephone: 01705 730639
Website:
www.letslinkuk.demon.co.uk

**Mail Preference Service Ltd.**
Telephone: 0345 034599

**Ministry of Agriculture, Fisheries and Food**
Whitehall Place West
London SW1A 2HH
Telephone: 0171 270 3000
Website: www.maff.gov.uk

**Natural Collection**
PO Box 2111
Bath BA1 2ZQ
Telephone: 01225 442288
Website: www.greenstore.co.uk

**Oxfam**
274 Banbury Road
Oxford OX2 7DZ
Telephone: 01865 312409
Website: www.oxfam.org.uk

**The Ramblers**
1-5 Wandsworth Road
London SW8 2XX
Telephone: 0207 339 8500
E-mail:
ramblers@london.ramblers.org.uk
Website: www.ramblers.org.uk

**Royal Society for the Protection of Birds (RSPB)**
The Lodge
Sandy
Bedfordshire SG19 2DL
Telephone: 01767 680551
Website: www.rspb.org.uk

**The Soil Association**
Bristol House
40-56 Victoria Street
Bristol BS1 6BY
Telephone: 0117 929 0661
E-mail: info@soilassociation.org
Website:
www.soilassociation.org

## The Solar Energy Society

C/o School of Engineering
Oxford Brookes University
Gipsy Lane Campus
Headington
Oxford OX3 OBP
Telephone: 01865 484367
Email: uk-ises@brookes.ac.uk
Website: www.brookes.ac.uk/uk-ises

## Sustrans

35 King Street
Bristol BS1 4DZ
Telephone: 0117 926 8893
Website: www.sustrans.org.uk

## Techknowledgy

British Council Offices
13 Windsor Terrace
Newcastle-Upon-Tyne NE2 4HE
Telephone: 01573  228 400
Website: www.tky.org.uk

## Tonertec

Telephone: 0171 498 1988

## Tourism Concern

Stapleton House
277-281 Holloway Road
London N7 8HN
Telephone: 020 7753 3330
Email:
info@tourismconcern.org.uk
Website:
www.tourismconcern.org.uk

## Transport 2000

Walkden House
10 Melton Street
London NW1
Telephone: 0171 388 8386

## United Kingdom Parliament

House of Commons
London SW1A 0AA
Information Office Telephone:
020 7219 4272
Website: www.parliament.uk

## Wastewatch

Europa House
Ground Floor
13-17 Ironmonger Row
London EC1U 3QG
Telephone: 0171 253 6266
Website:
www.wastewatch.org.uk

## The Wildlife Trusts

The Kiln
Waterside
Mather Road
Newark NG24 1WT
Telephone: 01636 677711

## Women's Environmental Network

87 Worship Street
London EC2A 2BE
Telephone: 0171 247 3327
E-mail: wenuk@gn.apc.org
Website: www.gn.apc.org/wen

## The Woodland Trust
Autumn Park
Grantham
Lincolnshire NG31 6LL
Telephone: 01476 581111

## WWF-UK
Panda House
Weyside Park
Godalming
Surrey GU7 1XR
Telephone: 01483 426444
Email: wwf-uk@wwf-uk.org
Website: www.wwf-uk.org

# Banks and Money

## The Co-operative Bank
PO Box 101
1 Balloon Street
Manchester M60 4EP
Tel 0161 832 3456

## Ecology Building Society
8 Main Street
Crosshills
Keighly
W. Yorkshire BD20 8TT
Telephone: 01535 635933

## Eiris
80-84 Bondway
London SW8 1SF
Telephone: 0107 840 5700
Website: www.eiris.org

## Shared Interest Society Ltd
25 Collingwood Street
Newcastle-Upon-Tyne
Tyne and Wear NE1 1JE
Telephone: 0191 233 9100
Email: post@shared-interest.com
Website: www.shared-interest.com

## Triodos Bank
Brunel House
11 The Promenade
Clifton
Bristol BS8 3NN
Telephone: 0117 973 9339

# Further Reading

- **Chris Baines** How to Make a Wildlife Garden (Elm Tree Books) 1986
- **Joanna Blythman** The Food We Eat (Penguin) 1998
- **Lynda Brown** The Shopper's Guide to Organic Food (Fourth Estate Ltd) 1998
- **Sue Dibb** What the Label Doesn't Tell You (Thorsons) 1998
- **FOE** The Polluting Factory Campaign Guide 1998
- **FOE** Fighting Road Schemes 1995
- **FOE** Saving Wildlife Sites 1994
- **FOE** The Landfill Campaign Guide 1997
- **FOE** The Incineration Campaign Guide 1998
- **FOE** Stopping the Sprawl: The Housing Campaign Guide 1997
- **FOE** The Good Wood Guide 1996
- **Geoff Hamilton** The Organic Gardening Book (Dorling Kindersley) 1997
- **Maurice Hanssen** E for Additives (Thorsons) 1987
- **Oliver James** Britain on the Couch (Arrow Books) 1998
- **Anthony Jay** How to Beat Sir Humphrey (Long Barn Books) 1997
- **The Soil Association** Where to Buy Organic Food (1998) (Available direct from SA)
- **B C Wolverton** Eco-friendly Houseplants: 50 Indoor Plants that Purify the Air (Phoenix) 1997

# Index

# E

Ecology Building Society 108, 125
Economic growth 105
Electrical appliances 84
Electricity suppliers 85
Energy Action Grants Agency 85, 122
Energy Efficiency Advice Centres 83, 85, 122
Energy Saving Trust 85, 122
Ethical Consumer Magazine 53, 64, 102, 115, 122
Ethical investment 107-109
Ethical Investment Research Service (Eiris) 109, 125
Ethical Trading Initiative 100, 102
European Community Energy Label 84
European Eco-label 58, 84

# F

Fabrics 98-99
Fabric dyes 99
Fairtrade Foundation 43, 100, 122
Fairtrade label 43
Fast food 24
Fish 27-28, 29
Food additives 24-25
Food Commission 39, 122
Food irradiation 34, 43
Food miles 44, 92

Food scares 31-32
Forest Stewardship Council 72, 76
Formaldehyde (see VOCs)
Free range food 42
Freedom Foods 42
Freewheelers 90, 94, 122
Friends of the Earth 39, 85, 92, 112, 116, 118, 122
Fur 100-101
Furniture Recycling Network 59, 122

# G

Gadgets 75-76
Global travel 91-92
Global warming 54, 73, 79, 80, 88, 91-92
Globalisation of trade 88
GM foods 36-39, 43, 46, 111
Green energy 83
Greenhouse effect 73, 80
Greenpeace 53, 112, 122

# H

Heating 82-83
Help the Aged 59, 123
Hemp 99
Henry Doubleday Research Association 66-67, 68, 123
Home decoration 74-75
Home Energy Efficiency Grant Scheme 85
Hydrofluorocarbons (HFCs) 53

Roadbuilding 91, 94
RSPB 100, 111, 118, 123

## S

Shared Interest Society Ltd
108, 125
Silk 99
Sites of Special Scientific
Interest (SSSIs) 88, 116
Slug Pellets 67
Soil Association 39, 41, 42,
47, 123
Soil erosion 33, 46
Solar Energy Society 83, 124
Stock market investments 109
Surfactants 54
Sustrans 124

## T

Techknowledgy 59, 124
Tonertec 59, 124
Tourism 91-93, 94
Tourism Concern 94, 124
Transport 2000 124
Triodos Bank 108, 125

## U

UK Parliament 113, 116, 124
UK Register of Organic Food
Standards 41

## V

Vegans 27, 99
Vegetarians 27-28
Ventilation 75
Viscose 98
Volatile organic compounds
(VOCs) 51, 58, 71-72, 73, 75,
76, 81, 102
Volunteers 118

## W

Wall insulation 81
Wastewatch 59, 124
Water conservation 57, 69
Water supply 53, 54, 98, 99
Wildlife 28, 61, 65-66
Wildlife Trusts 116, 118, 124
Women's Environmental
Network 102, 124
Wood and forest products 72
Woodland Trust, the 124
Woodwork protection 73-74
Wool 98
Work 104-105
World hunger 33, 38-39
WWF-UK 125